BY RICH WINOGRAD

A Publication of

THE NAPOLEON HILL FOUNDATION

Published by:
The Napoleon Hill Foundation
P. O. Box 1277
Wise, Virginia 24293

Website: www.naphill.org
Email: napoleonhill@uvawise.edu

ISBN: 0-9771463-6-7

I read *Paloma* in one sitting....not because it is brief but rather because it is thought provoking. *Paloma* documents God's active presence and participation in the life of man. It shows how faith provides the medium for recognizing this and for accepting it.

JAMES BLAIR HILL, MD

In his book *Paloma,* Rich Winograd shares with us a more than special story of a little girl and her family who experience the joys, challenges, puzzles and love of contemporary family life. Winograd's mission is similar to Paloma's; to open our hearts to possibilities within ourselves. Paloma and Napoleon Hill share the ability to use the concepts of Applied Faith, Cosmic Habitforce and Living through Adversity and Defeat to achieve a Definiteness of Purpose in family life. This read will make you smile through tears, see hope in the clouds and rest easier knowing success, both spiritual and earthly, is within us all.

JUDITH B. ARCY, PHD

This is an amazing story of a loving bond between a mother and her young daughter. It is a story of serendipity, spirituality and a reminder that we are all living spirits having a human body experience. When you read this book you will realize that everything happens for a reason. This is a book every family should have in their library.

FRED WIKKELING
AUTHOR OF *LOOK UP!*

Once in a while, there comes a book so beautiful, so filled with love, so filled with faith, no one should miss it. *Paloma* is that story. Every mother, teacher, parent, grandparent, and anyone who wants to be a parent should read this story of love and faith.

BARBARA GARDNER, MED.

Paloma is the moving tale of a beautiful and profound young life. It is also a touching story of faith, love, hope, and family that all can appreciate and enjoy.

MARY AKERS, CO-AUTHOR OF *RADICAL GRATITUDE AND OTHER LIFE LESSONS LEARNED IN SIBERIA*

I could hardly put ***Paloma*** down!! I read it into the night. What a touching and wonderful story for the parents to share.

GAYNELL LARSEN

Paloma, dove, is a beautiful story of the fragility and strength of life. We imagine we are the real architects of our lives. Quiet trust allows us to see the meaning of love and the presence of God in the color and texture of everyday circumstances. We are given persons who come into our lives for a short while. We pass through joy and pain, confusion and doubt. We are not meant to remain here. Each day is an invitation to see, to feel, to live, to love. All good is given us by a loving Providence that draws us to life eternal. Faith lets us begin to live that life now in part.

SR. THERESE GUERIN SULLIVAN SP
CHANCELLOR OF THE
DIOCESE OF CLEVELAND

The author skillfully shows us that everything happens for a reason. Infinite Intelligence has given us our children to teach and remind us to have faith. ***Paloma*** is a gift of life.

CHRISTINA CHIA
CHAIRMAN AND FOUNDER OF
NAPOLEON HILL ASSOCIATES

Paloma is a spiritually precocious, straightforward girl with deep feelings and a strong will. The relationship between her and her mother Elida is very special. Elida sees much of herself in her daughter and believes that God is working in Paloma in an extraordinary way. Miracles happen every day if only we have the eyes to see them. This book leaves me with the same feeling that I often have when someone has shared with me some elements of their heart's journey. In those moments I often feel that I have been walking on sacred ground.

REV. ROBERT SIPE
CATHOLIC CHAPLAIN
PORT OF DULUTH

Paloma is a deeply religious story without being "preachy." Although we do not know Paloma personally, we come to realize that she understands her purpose for living in an almost mystical way. Rich Winograd has done a masterful job of communicating with the reader this inner-knowledge of this young girl. This book will touch the lives of all who read it.

Fr. John W. Love
Holy Cross Catholic Church
Moorpark, California

One needs only to know a small child to feel the energy of this book. Between the mother's human heart, a daughter's spiritual soul, and the facts crafted by the author, the reader is able to see that the world is, without question, all about faith, hope and love.

Thomas E. Konrady
Porto Alegre, RS-Brazil

Paloma is an important story. People will see themselves throughout this book – whether they identify with this remarkable young girl, her loving parents, or perhaps even her siblings. Maybe you know people like Paloma, who are wise beyond their years. Their presence graces our lives as they remind us to partake of the many blessings that await us with each new day.

Robin Jay
Award-winning Author
and Motivational Speaker

Paloma is a book that offers an abundance of hope to others. It puts life into perspective. Having stirred my emotions, it made me reflect on my life and the significance of having an attitude of gratitude for what life brings us day by day. The chief blessing in this book is the knowledge that everything happens for a reason. The reader is indebted to *Paloma* for reminding us to trust, have faith and that love is everlasting.

Dan Gibbons
Loving Husband and Father
Motivational Speaker and Seminar Presenter

Beautifully written, richly descriptive, the story of Paloma reaches that place of deep longing in each of our hearts. Sometimes "why?" can never be fully understood or answered, but with open minds and hearts, we can learn great lessons, especially from our children. Read and be prepared to look at life with renewed awe and respect, enhanced with faith and hope.

JIM CONNELLY
AUTHOR OF *ONE MORE SUNSET*

Life is a series of pieces to a puzzle that connect us in ways in which we may not fully understand until we navigate our way through life's adversities. ***Paloma*** helps us realize how delicate the puzzle pieces of life are.

KELLY S. KING
DIRECTOR OF EDUCATION AND PRODUCT DEVELOPMENT
KELLY S. KING ACADEMY AND MODERN MASTERS INC.

I'm reminded to live life to its fullest and recognize my purpose in this world. ***Paloma*** reminds me that changing lives "one at a time" doesn't stop with just one person – it's passed on.

SHANNON MUHS, MS, RD, LMNT
REGISTERED DIETITIAN AND
LICENSED MEDICAL NUTRITION THERAPIST

Written in a simple and beautiful style, this is a story of a little girl who teaches us great spiritual principles. It's about power of hope, strength of faith, learning from adversity and about love. Once you start reading it, you will not be able to put it down.

ANDY BIENKOWSKI
CO-AUTHOR OF *RADICAL GRATITUDE*

Dedication

Many thanks . . .

to Paloma and Elida for your faith,
hope, light and inspiration;

to Orpet, Renata and Tiago;

to Deborah, Tatiana and especially
Regina for your love and support;

to Antonio for your musical inspiration;

to Judith Williamson
for your wisdom and guidance;

to Don Green and Bob Johnson
for your trust and support;

to Napoleon Hill for the teachings of life's
true riches and how to attain them;

and to God for all of the reasons that
have become evident and for all of the
reasons that have yet to be discovered.

Introduction

By Judy Williamson
Director of the Napoleon Hill World Learning Center

Some books are meant to be read for entertainment and some books are meant to crack open your heart and allow "the thing with feathers" to enter and instill hope. ***Paloma*** is just such a book. It is a book with a mission, not simply a theme. Its mission is to provide hope to people whose experiences in life require the power of hope and the strength of faith.

Pain, misfortune, suffering and loss can occur in many ways. It can happen when relationships end, children leave home, families separate and of course when loved ones die. Hope, however, can spring eternal and bring healing to the torn, ragged edges of individual grief. The story of ***Paloma*** provides the point of connection for the miracle of healing to begin.

While reading this work of non-fiction, I was immediately touched with the universality of what the author, Rich Winograd, has immortalized for the reader. Not only has he told the story of a young girl's mission in life, but also the story of every individual who is faced with the task of asking and answering the unanswerable question of why things happen the way they do.

Paloma differs from the norm, however, because this book does answer the unanswerable question in the only acceptable way – faith. Faith has been biblically defined as the substance of things hoped for, the evidence of things not seen. Hope lives in the future. It is a belief that things will improve over time. During periods of pain, misfortune, suffering and loss, hope is the only thing that keeps many people from literal and spiritual death. ***Paloma*** demonstrates firsthand how a family can rise from the ashes like the mythological Phoenix to experience rebirth.

Poetry often conceptualizes in words what is best understood in the heart. The poem entitled "Hope" by Emily Dickinson metaphorically captures the abstract concept of hope by describing it as a bird that lives within one's soul ever ready to warm a person during the toughest times. Ironically, Paloma's name means dove, and the dove not only symbolizes love, friendship, and peace but can also represent the carrier of a message. It was a dove that came to Noah in the evening carrying in its beak an olive leaf. By this message, Noah knew that the waters flooding the earth had subsided and it was safe to go ashore. Paloma delivers the same message - be not afraid, rather know that life beyond this life exists. Her mission was to deliver this message just as it was Christ's mission to send the Holy Spirit, depicted also as a dove, to bolster the apostles and disciples in their mission to spread the gospel without fear. Paloma fearlessly delivers the message that hope is best expressed through faith in things unseen.

Consider the positive message in Emily Dickinson's poem below:

Hope

Hope is the thing with feathers
That perches in the soul,
And sings the tune–without the words,
And never stops at all,
And sweetest in the gale is heard;
And sore must be the storm
That could abash the little bird
That kept so many warm.
I've heard it in the chillest land,
And on the strangest sea;
Yet, never, in extremity,
It asked a crumb of me.

EMILY DICKINSON

Author Rich Winograd was inspired to write this book when he learned of Paloma's circumstances. He credits several sources as preparatory for this valuable work. Dr. Napoleon Hill's ***Think and Grow Rich*** is one of them. As the Director of the Napoleon Hill World Learning Center at Purdue University Calumet, I cannot help but see the synchronicities between this work and Dr. Hill's principles of success. Having taught the PMA Science of Success Course numerous times, it is apparent that the principles of Applied Faith, Learning from Adversity and Defeat, Cosmic Habitforce, and Definiteness of Purpose are imbedded in this writing. Consequently, ***Paloma*** serves as an excellent real life example of Dr. Hill's lessons.

In an article entitled "This Changing World," Dr. Hill states:

> *Yes, I know, now, that my Faith in Infinite Intelligence is real and enduring. It is not a blind faith; it is a faith based upon close examination of the handiwork of this Intelligence. I had been looking for evidence of the source of my faith in the wrong direction; seeking it in the deeds of men.*
>
> *I found it in a tiny acorn and a giant oak tree, in the leaflets of a humble fern and in the soil of the earth; in the friendly sun which warms the earth and gives motion to the waters; in a tiny pebble of stone and in the Evening Star, in the silence and the calm of the great outdoors.*

Dr. Hill finds evidence of his faith in nature, and the workings of Cosmic Habitforce in the law and order of the universe. He encounters this only after experiencing the collapse of his bank and loss of his funds during the Great Depression. Life provides many teachers but the same lesson. Each of us is put here to fulfill a divine mission. Some of us recognize it from the beginning as did Paloma. Others strive to uncover our definite major purpose. Regardless of how we find it, the meaning is that no life is pointless or without value. We are put here to be of service by a benevolent creator who knows our worth because each of us is made in His divine image and likeness. As we work to uncover our purpose most of us struggle with faith, learn from adversity and defeat, and strive to understand the meaning of life. These themes are universal and represent the most significant things that happen in our life.

Is it any wonder that the beautiful and vivacious Paloma would be put here to deliver a lesson of hope and healing for each and every one of us? Her ultimate message is that life goes on. Not just physical life, but spiritual life. Because we come from the stars we will shine on. Paloma knew this when she wrote: "To believe is truth in a hope that we have the creation of life." Dr. Napoleon Hill put it another way: "What the mind can conceive and believe, the mind can achieve." Each is correct.

In closing, I would like to publicly thank the author, Rich Winograd, for gifting this book to the Napoleon Hill World Learning Center for its educational programs. Rich has received no compensation for this book because he feels that it has a life and mission of its own. He also understands that you give to give, not give to get. I agree. We are all but conduits for the work of Infinite Intelligence. I know that I speak for the author and myself when I state that you will be blessed by this book. It will change your life because it is a true story and carries the message of everlasting life. Enjoy it. Benefit from it. And pass it on because each one of us is undergoing the human experience and needs all the very real help that is available in times of trouble.

With gratitude to Rich Winograd for his phenomenal gift of ***Paloma***! May your life be blessed in a reciprocal way!

JUDY WILLIAMSON

Paloma Palmeira Peixoto was born on
June 11, 1981 in São Paulo, Brazil
where her family still lives.

BY RICH WINOGRAD

The following is
based on a true story

"To believe is truth
in a hope that we have
the creation of life."

Chapter 1

Everything happens for a reason.

This simple philosophy is often doubted, disputed or disregarded because the reasons are not immediately evident and thus a void is created; a void that creates doubt, dispute and disregard. But those with faith and hope have the patience and the wisdom to seek the reasons.

Faith takes many forms. The process of seeking life's reasons also takes many forms. There is no singular way; there are many ways. Scholars, educators, and religious leaders have espoused the ways throughout the ages, but ultimately it is a personal and private task. God works in mysterious ways and cloaks the reasons in the most mysterious of circumstances. When faith is applied, reasons appear.

In Brazil, for example, faith and reasons are found in many places. For some, Brazil's pure and natural beauty is a source of energizing faith and hope. Brazil's myriad diversity of beauty and splendor rolls in the waves that kiss the white sanded beaches of Fortaleza and Natal. Its beauty soars on the wings of a multi-colored macaw that floats amongst the rich, lush trees in the Amazon. Its splendor creates a delicious aroma inside a short cup of coffee that's brewed in a lazy outdoor cafe on a slow afternoon in Belo Horizonte.

Brazil's beauty can be heard in the mesmerizing musical beat of a samba school that plays endlessly into the night during Carnival. It can be seen in the constant flow of water that pours from high above the Falls of Iguacu. It can be tasted in the delectably sweet papaya or mango purchased at an outdoor market in the growing, modern city of São Paulo and smelled above a simmering kettle of fresh shrimp and coconut, slowly stirred in a spicy sauce by a skillful Bahian cook. And it can be touched on the heartbeat of any soccer fan who has ever watched a Brazilian "futebol" player maneuver towards the goal in a World Cup match.

But nowhere, perhaps even in the world, can more beauty and splendor and energizing faith and hope be experienced than in Brazil's flamboyant city of Rio de Janeiro. From the earliest Portuguese explorers to the 17th Century Benedictine monks, to historians, and modern day writers and poets, many have exhausted their imaginative vocabularies trying to describe Rio. One writer eloquently and simply stated that it's less a series of items than it is an impression.

From high atop the Corcovado, the massive statue of Christ the Redeemer, such an impression can be felt. The gorgeous panorama of mountains and sea, which includes the Sugarloaf, the Botafogo Bay and the picturesque beaches of Copacabana and Ipanema gives an impression. And down below, on the leisurely paced streets of a city with simple life values and strong family values, such an impression can be felt.

But the mystery of faith, especially in Brazil, lies beyond the picture perfect images of beauty and splendor. The faces of poverty and hunger and deprivation also seek reasons. Shirtless men with scruffy beards who sit motionless on the stoops of small tire repair garages cling to their faith. Barefoot children, no more than six years of age, who offer chewing gum and tissues for sale at every street corner also have hope. A disheveled woman who sprawls out on a sidewalk with a bundle of torn blankets surrounding her and her three tiny children also longs for reasons. In the stench of burning garbage that fills the air of a hillside slum village are lives longing for an explanation.

For many, rich and poor alike, reasons are found in the churches. A church in Brazil is as much a museum as it is a place of worship. Marble sculptures, rich gold carvings from Portugal, finely carved furniture made from the Brazilian jacaranda wood, elaborate silver lamps, huge rosewood chests of drawers with silver handles, walls of Portuguese tile and alabaster figures of saints help create a magnificent impression of faith and hope. The churches are impeccably clean.

* * * * * * *

On a brilliantly sunny summer morning sometime in the 1950s, in front of a small church that nestled amongst the trees on a hillside road, parishioners mingled and exchanged hugs and Brazilian kisses, a gentle touch on both sides of the face. A Mass had just ended and another glorious day of faith and hope had just begun.

The entrance to the church was lined with blooming mimosa and vibrant bougainvillea. Inside the foyer the soft sounds of an organ bounced off the hard wood floors. A few people remained inside the sanctuary; silently praying, quietly talking or doing whatever it is that they felt inspired to do.

Most notably, especially to the priest who observed this from the corner of his eye as he spoke privately to an older woman, was a young girl who slowly and cautiously approached the altar. She was finely attired in a delicate white dress with lace, short white socks, and polished black shoes. Her blonde hair was neatly combed and her face was clean and fresh. She carried with her a bouquet of pink roses.

As she stood in front of the altar, both the priest and the older woman turned their attention more towards the girl. They watched in wonder and curiosity as the little girl tried to place the flowers on the top of the altar. She seemed intent on reaching but after trying several times she opted to place them on the floor in front. She seemed satisfied, not frustrated, so neither the priest nor the older woman offered their help as they both considered doing.

The older woman did approach the little girl as she walked away from the altar. She knelt down and smiled and reached out to touch the lace that dangled from the front of her dress.

"What is your name?" the older woman asked in a soft and loving voice.

"Elida," the girl replied shortly, but politely.

"That's a very pretty name," the woman continued. "And the pink roses you had are very pretty too."

"Thank you," Elida replied again, shortly and politely.

Elida joined her parents, sister and little brother, at the back of the church and together they stepped outside into the hot sun. Elida's father, a thin and tall man who made a decent, middle-class living in the Air Force, lit a cigarette and walked alone to get the car. Dora, Elida's mother, waited underneath the shade of a eucalyptus tree with her three children. Dora stared awkwardly at Elida for a moment and then realized why. She didn't have the flowers, the expensive bouquet of pink roses that she had brought with her to the Mass.

"Elida, we were going to put them on the table at home to decorate our Sunday night dinner."

Elida shrugged and offered neither an explanation nor a reason. She left the flowers at the altar and that was all, for now.

Everything happens for a reason.

* * * * * * *

Across town, in a part of Rio called Tijuca, stood a house that evoked almost as much feeling and character as a church. Built in 1898 on a beautifully barren strip of land which came to be called Rua Campos Sales, this house stood by and watched patiently as the city grew up around it. It also stood up, strong and bold, comforting and supportive, as a remarkable family grew up inside it.

Marques Peixoto. The letters MP and the year, 1898 were carved in stone on the face of the house, high atop the second floor veranda. Orpet Jose Marques Peixoto, who was born and would die in the very same house on Rua Campos Sales, stood near the door in front of his house and playfully cavorted with the neighbors. A lawyer, police officer and sheriff, Orpet wielded some influence, but not as much as he could have had he been more committed to his career. Instead, he spent time just enjoying his life. He liked homemade food and ice cream and he enjoyed an occasional scotch with his friends and family members. He also loved children, and there would be a lot to love.

A young man already engaged to marry another, Orpet hopped a bus one day in Rio, spotted a lovely young woman named Lourdes and changed his mind and his plans in a hurry. The two married and with him being very fun-loving and she being very Catholic, they produced ten children.

Orpet continued talking in front of the house while upstairs his uncle organized a small suitcase. Being one of the few members of the family to own a car, Orpet willingly volunteered to drive his uncle to the interstate bus station. Also along for the day's ride was a detective associate of Orpet's who came home for lunch and of course, the six young children who raced excitedly down the stairs to join in on the excursion.

The line of children piled one by one into the family's old, but distinguished Chrysler road car. Lourdes, wearing a kitchen apron that covered her protruding belly, containing child number seven, watched patiently. With everyone reasonably in place, Orpet kissed his wife good-bye and slowly steered his vehicle away from the curb. The intense summer heat of Rio made a quick stop for ice cream a must. The blazing sun pounded against the wide glass pane of the Chrysler which forced the children to lick their cones quickly to keep pace with the rapid melting process. They giggled and licked and passed their cones amongst each other and licked some more as their father sped quickly through the streets of Tijuca towards the higher, elevated part of town, which would provide a cooler and more scenic route to the bus station.

Sitting in the back seat, on the farthest right side, with his small shoulder pressed up against the door, was a 4-year old, Orpet Jose Marques Peixoto, Jr., or Petinho to use the Portuguese diminutive. He sat more quietly than his brothers and sisters and refrained from exchanging his cone with the others. Intently he worked on his own cone while attempting to see outside the window.

As the Chrysler twisted and turned through the streets of the city, Orpet spoke with his uncle. He talked mainly about the Brazilian government, or lack of it. He sped ahead as he reached the Alto da Boa Vista, a winding, scenic stretch that headed high above the city and then dropped down to the beach on the other side. As the car climbed the temperature lowered just a bit and the air lightened. As Orpet drove he peered over the side of the road at the city below and felt an undeserved feeling of superiority.

The children screeched and cheered as the Chrysler picked up speed on the curves. The broad tires of the car screeched as well as Orpet took each new turn at full speed. And then, in a sudden and jolting moment, the voices quieted and silence overcame the back seat as there was one less passenger. The right side door of the back seat had somehow swung open on a curve and little Orpet went tumbling onto the road.

The silence and shock lasted just a second. Immediately after the older children screamed at their father who had not yet seen what had happened, he slammed on the brakes and pulled sharply to the side of the road. As he jumped out and looked back he saw his son standing on the side of the road.

What had happened actually was nothing at all. As his small, but chunky body rolled out of the car, it took one spin in the dirt and then propelled him onto his feet. He suffered not even a scratch. He stood calmly and quietly on the side of the road as his father and all the others came to see how he was. His face showed little emotion at all.

In the open air kitchen on Rua Campos Sales, Lourdes slowly stirred a hot kettle of black beans. Suddenly, the screaming voices from the stairway turned her attention away from the stove.

"Mommy, Petinho fell out of the car!" the oldest son yelled out.

"He fell out of the car!" repeated another.

With a look of horror, Lourdes stood at the top of the stairway and watched as the parade of juvenile news reporters came running.

"Orpet!" she called out to her husband. "Orpet, what happened?"

"Everything's fine," he yelled from the bottom of the stairway, "just a small accident, but nothing more."

Lourdes raced down the stairs as little Orpet entered the doorway. She hugged her son tightly and kissed his unblemished forehead. Horrific thoughts of a more serious accident filled her head. She looked in his eyes, breathed a sigh of relief and smiled.

Orpet shrugged and offered neither an explanation nor a reason. He had fallen out of the car and that was all, for now.

Everything happens for a reason.

Chapter 2

Ponies. She was surrounded by ponies.

Not real ponies of course. There could be no logical purpose for having real ponies in a child's bedroom and purpose is exactly what defined Paloma's world.

These were the little, rubber ponies that galloped onto the shelves of toy stores just about the time that Cabbage Patch dolls were wilting in popularity. They stood about five inches high and measured the same five inches in length. Their eyes were extremely large for their small bodies, marking their pensiveness and inquisitiveness. Some had their heads cocked as if they were thinking or wanting to say something. Some had a leg bent in apparent motion as if they were going somewhere. Others even had small wings, displaying an even greater and perhaps divine notion that they were going somewhere.

The inscription on the back left foot of the ponies indicated that they had come from Hong Kong but to Paloma they were delivered straight from heaven. These were not merely toys, they were her prized possessions. They required the same amount of love and care that one would give to a child. And Paloma gave, laboriously and affectionately.

With a damp cloth she slowly caressed the bodies of each of her eleven ponies to remove the dust and debris that had accumulated from the day before. She had twelve ponies but the one that she received one week earlier, on her seventh birthday, was still encased in its original wrapping. So enamored by the purity of a new pony, Paloma normally kept each one wrapped for a few weeks before unleashing it into the world.

She moved the cloth gently around the face of each pony to avoid getting any soapy water in the eyes or mouth. Her father once washed her mouth with soapy water when she cried too much for no apparent reason and then called everyone around her stupid. That awful taste was so vivid in her memory that she tried her best to avoid putting the ponies through the same anguish.

It was a slow and tedious process but one that was necessary in order to maintain the beauty of the ponies. Each pony was a different color and it was Paloma's primary concern that the colors would not lose their brilliance with age. The charm of carnation pink, the freshness of springtime green, the shine of sun-drenched yellow, and the sparkle of aqua blue all had to be preserved.

"Sit still," she told the navy blue pony as she cleaned behind his front legs. He had spent the day before outside taking part in the picnic that Paloma had hosted to celebrate Brazil's "June" holiday, and he had built up a considerable amount of dirt during the festivities.

"If you don't let me finish cleaning you up, I won't let you go outside for a whole week," she commanded. Her authoritative voice and the fact that one other pony had already received this punishment was reason enough for the navy blue pony to subdue itself from whatever antics it had been up to. Paloma seemed proud of her successful display of authority and politely but sternly said thank you to the now obedient little subject.

After the ponies were all cleaned, Paloma lined them up for the other important and time consuming part of the daily beautification process–the combing of the hair. The ponies had long, flowing manes which needed to be disciplined and tamed. Having a full head of long, blonde hair herself, Paloma had become quite adept with a comb. And not just any comb;

she had a wide variety of instruments designed to tackle any problem that the ponies presented.

Individually she went; straightening one, curling another, braiding, knotting, teasing and lacing. Wielding the comb with the precision that a painter uses with his brush, she shaped and fashioned each pony into perfect elegance.

"Mommy, where are you?" Paloma called out from her bedroom.

"I'm in my bathroom sweetie," Elida replied almost immediately.

Paloma carefully organized the ponies in their respective places on the shelf and then scurried down the hallway. She stopped at the bathroom that she shared with her sister and brother to pick up her white stepping stool. She continued down the hallway, through her parent's bedroom and into the master bedroom where her mother had already begun her daily beautification process. She placed the stool alongside the sink, perching herself in position to watch and learn about the art of being a woman.

"Nobody does it better," Elida sang one of her favorite American songs with a Brazilian accent, "...makes me feel sad for the rest."

"Don't sing, Mommy," Paloma said from her stepping stool.

"Nobody does it half as good as you," Elida continued. "Baby you're the best."

"Mommy, don't sing."

"What do you mean, don't sing? I like to sing."

"But I don't like it."

"Oh, you're so silly. What have you been doing, alone in your room so quietly?"

"Getting my ponies ready."

"Ready for what?"

"For a party. They're going to a birthday party."

"Whose birthday is it?"

"It's nobody's birthday, Mommy. You know, it's just play."

Elida chuckled, embarrassed for a moment that she had failed to follow her daughter's reality. Their ability to communicate, both in and out of play, was so fine-tuned, but occasionally Paloma would mix the two and catch Elida off guard.

With the coloring gel lathered in her hands, Elida began massaging her scalp, seeking and destroying the strands of gray that had so uninvitingly crept between the strands of her golden brown hair. At 39, she could have very easily blamed age, work and the rigors of raising three children for a decline in her appearance. Instead, she took great strides to assure that the girl who Orpet fell in love with twenty-two years before would always look her best.

The forty or fifty dollars that she spent every so often at the salon was as important, she insisted, as the money Orpet spent on his computer software. She had no objection to doing her hair at home and she could do it quite well, but when she decided that a professional's touch was necessary, she went and paid without second thoughts.

Likewise, a new outfit at a reasonable price was as important as a new pair of sneakers for Tiago and her art supplies and art classes were as mandatory as Renata's swim team practices and Paloma's ballet lessons.

With as much patience and understanding as his frugal mind could muster, Orpet allowed his wife to do what she needed to do. While normally he got by with as little as possible and checked every receipt to see if even less was possible, Elida spent and acted freely. Somehow it managed to work, both within the marriage and within the checkbook.

The gel was now fully lathered throughout her hair, the rancid odor that it gave had permeated the bathroom and for the time being, Elida looked anything but beautiful.

"What are you doing Mom?" Paloma asked in disbelief.

"I'm dyeing my hair."

"You mean your hair's going to die?"

"Very funny. I'm coloring it; painting it."

"Why do you want to paint your hair?"

"Well, as you get older, your hair loses some of its shine and its color, just like with your ponies. You have to take care of the hair so it stays shiny and pretty."

"Well, I think it looks gross. I don't ever want to paint my hair. I don't want to get older if that's what you have to do. I'll just stay a kid forever."

Elida smiled and gazed down at her little girl and her shiny blonde hair which was streaked with the morning sunlight that had entered through the bathroom window. Deep inside, that is exactly what Elida wanted too. As wonderful as it was to see her daughter grow, she felt threatened by this particular passage of time. Since this was her last child, she found her maternal instincts wanting to hold on longer to each day. She coveted Paloma's childhood a bit more so than she did the childhood of both Renata and Tiago.

She remembers how agitated her stomach felt the day that she packed away, for the last time, the baby clothes, the pacifiers and the bottles. She was thrilled that Orpet's cousin would be able to use them, but seeing them go was not easy.

Now, each pair of blue jeans or sneakers that Paloma outgrew served as a painful notice that the hands of time were not standing still. She reached down and hugged Paloma, holding on as best she could.

"Is this your go-out day with Daddy?"

"Yes. Why?"

"I just could tell. That's why you're making yourself so pretty."

"I have to make myself pretty for Daddy and we have to go out on dates together. If not, he might want to find another wife."

"No Mommy, you're the only wife. You're beautiful."

"Thank you, sweetie."

"Where are you and Daddy going dating?"

"I'm not sure. Your father likes to surprise me. Maybe we'll go to a show or to a movie or maybe we'll go to a restaurant for dinner."

"You know, I have a good idea Mommy. How about if the babysitter goes on the date with Daddy and you stay here with me."

"Oh Paloma," Elida laughed. It was the kind of suggestion that made their relationship so special. "I want to be with you, but I want to be alone with your father also. Besides, we have a whole lifetime together."

"Do we?"

"Of course we do."

"How long is a lifetime, Mommy?"

"A long time Paloma; a long, long time."

"Are you sure?"

Elida became puzzled. She reached down and hugged Paloma once again.

"I love you."

"I love you too."

Elida gently ran her fingers through Paloma's hair as the two stood quietly in the bathroom for a brief, but precious moment.

"Why don't you run along to your room and find something to do while I shower," Elida said as she helped Paloma off of the stool. "I'll just be a minute and then you can help me prepare some lunch."

"Don't waste too much water," Paloma replied as she picked up the stool and scampered out of the bathroom. "And don't sing in the shower."

Paloma quickly checked on her ponies as she entered her bedroom and then sat herself down at the small white desk that stood under the room's lone window. The soft pink curtains with the bright pink roses were open, which allowed the bright sunlight to overwhelm the top of the desk. Paloma reached into the top drawer and pulled out a pair of plastic sun glasses which she placed onto her face with a childish sense of flair.

The view that Paloma took in through the clear plastic lenses consisted primarily of a long row of eucalyptus trees. Paloma talked often about the tall and stolid trees and she looked to them fondly on a daily basis. Their stature and presence, Elida observed, seemed to serve as a source of comfort to Paloma in much the same way that a child looks up to an adult. Elida also noted that Paloma was not in awe of the trees, the way a child might be of something so large. Instead, Elida explained to her sister one day, Paloma seemed to relate to them on an equal basis. Elida's sister was of the opinion that a relationship between a 7-year-old girl and a bunch of trees was extremely ludicrous; however, Elida maintained her faith and understanding in her daughter's interest in nature.

Paloma took her eyes away from the eucalyptus and turned her attention to a white envelope which sat atop the desk. She pulled out of the envelope a stack of white papers which she began leafing through with great intent. A few of the sheets were colorfully decorated with drawings of flowers and the others consisted only of words in a neatly styled handwriting.

Paloma picked up a pencil and began quickly tapping it on the desk, almost in rhythm with the faint sound of the water that made its way from Elida's shower. After removing her glasses, Paloma carefully made some marks on two of the sheets which were handwritten. She then folded one of the sheets in half and then in quarters and then placed the sheet inside the large breast pocket of her pink blouse. She reorganized the envelope and placed it in its original spot on the desk.

Paloma cast one more glance outside at the eucalyptus trees and then suddenly jumped out of her chair and walked out of the room. She tip-toed quietly down the hallway, paying particular attention to the sound of the water which continued in the shower. She entered her parent's bedroom, walked over to her mother's side of the bed and placed atop the night stand the folded piece of paper that was in her pocket. Like a mouse who had successfully found its cheese, Paloma then raced unnoticed out of the room.

Elida finished her shower without wasting too much water, nor had she sang a word, just as Paloma had asked. As she entered the bedroom draped in a salmon-colored towel, she immediately noticed the new addition to her night stand. Wiping dry her hair with a small, salmon-colored towel, Elida walked towards the night stand and sat at the edge of the bed. Slowly she unfolded the white piece of paper and began to read.

Para Mamãe

de Paloma

Eu te adoro você é a melhor coisa da minha

Vida

"To Mommy
From Paloma
I adore you, you are the best thing in my life"

Chapter 3

Orpet arrived home just after eleven o'clock.

Home was Lago Azul, or Blue Lake, an idyllic suburban community outside of São Paulo. There was more green grass, more green eucalyptus trees and more free birds in Lago Azul than people in São Paulo, the world's third largest city. Just as the big city was busy, Lago Azul was idle. As the city was noisy, Lago Azul was quiet.

Orpet drove slowly through the front gate of the guarded community and waved respectfully to Salvador, the guard on duty. The engine of his new car ruffled the feathers of a pair of geese who ambled near the road. He continued alongside the fairway of the first hole of the golf course that rolled between the various tracts of houses. The house that the Brazilian Navy had given him and his family upon their return from the United States was situated just off the green of the third hole and within walking distance of the tennis court and the pool. It was a large, spacious, five-bedroom ranch house and Orpet thoroughly enjoyed coming home to it. He enjoyed the tranquility that the community provided and enjoyed the recreation that was available. He had promised himself to take up golf, because as he saw it, that was the business thing to do, but he had yet to pick up a club. He picked up a tennis racket from time to time and also enjoyed the privacy and relaxation of their own private pool in the back yard.

He parked in the driveway in the front of the house, but walked around to the back door, primarily to say hello to Wolf, his baby Siberian Husky.

"Hello," he called out as he wrestled with Wolf and his gnawing young teeth. "How's everything?"

"Are you talking to me or to the dog?" Elida asked from the kitchen.

"To you, dear. I haven't taught Wolf how to talk just yet."

"How was your morning?" Elida inquired.

"It's over, let's put it that way. I tied up all the loose ends that I had to and I'm not going to worry about anything more for a few weeks."

"So that idea of teaching a winter course at the college never materialized?"

"Fortunately not. It wasn't a bad idea, but I really don't need that. What I need, what we need is a break."

"I agree. Where are we going tonight?"

"Out. How's that? The rest you'll know later. Just be ready by five o'clock. Your hair looks great by the way. Where are the kids?"

"Renata is at a friend's house. Tiago is out back playing golf, and Paloma is in her room. I'm putting together a little lunch. I told them to be at the table at twelve thirty."

"That's fine. I'm going into the office for awhile. Call me if you need anything. Oh, by the way, how's Paloma?"

"She's fine. Why?"

"Well, after I had that little skirmish with her last night, she went to bed and I didn't see her this morning."

"She asked where you were when she woke up but that was all."

"She drives me crazy sometimes, Elida. I mean it was so ridiculous last night. One minute she's sitting in the living room laughing and having fun with everyone, and the next minute she goes into a rage of temper."

"That's because you screamed at her, Orpet."

"I didn't scream at her. I told her to do something and she refused to do it."

"You screamed at her, Orpet. You don't realize how rough

you are on her sometimes."

"So you're saying it was my fault last night? That's beautiful. That's exactly what I wanted to come home to hear."

"Orpet, I'm not saying it's only your fault. I know Paloma has a temper and I know I have difficulty dealing with it at times. I just think that we both have to find a better way of relating to her. Don't make an issue of it, honey, please. Just go and say hello to her. That's all."

Orpet walked down the hallway to the office; he stopped briefly at the first bedroom on the left. He poked his head in quietly, not to disturb whatever was going on.

"Hello, Paloma. What are you doing?"

"I'm getting my ponies ready."

"Ready for what?"

"Dad, please. I already explained that to Mommy. Can you ask her?"

Orpet nodded, gave a half-smile, and walked away from the door.

The office, as Orpet had found the necessity to call it, was the one room in the house where the family's business matters were conducted. When they first moved into the house, before one piece of furniture was in place, Orpet mandated that the large bedroom adjacent to the master bedroom would be exclusively for business. He had patiently spent his whole career sharing accommodations with cookbooks, Barbie dolls, soccer balls and pet ponies. The time had come, he decided, to enjoy the executive privilege of having his own office in his home.

Elida had wanted the bedroom reserved for guests, while the children had a wide variety of suggestions on how the room could be used but the debate was brief and uneventful as Orpet had his mind made up. When it came to matters of career, business, finances and family politics, Orpet's opinions and decisions were rarely challenged. Not that he ruled his household with an iron fist; it's just that more times than not his reasoning worked out in the best interests of everyone. The office was no exception.

Initially the office was scantily clad, just as Orpet had wanted it. His habits were meticulous and precise and excessive furniture or decorations did not coincide with his organized mentality. In the middle of the room, to the left of the bay window which overlooked the pool and the fairway of the third hole, was a moderately sized, contemporary, oak desk. On the right side of the desk sat the computer which he bought in the United States and the printer he had picked up on a return visit. On the left side was a stack of papers, neatly piled at ninety degree angles to the corner of the desk. Along the middle sat in organized sequence a Cross pen set, a telephone message center, a brass lamp, a calendar, and a picture frame with two photos–the wedding picture in which Elida snuck a kiss on his ear just as the photographer clicked what was supposed to be a formal shot and the photo of the three children in the arms of Mickey Mouse which they took on their last visit to Disneyland.

The only other piece of furniture in the office when it was first inhabited was a black leather chair which Orpet moved to when his wooden desk chair began getting the best of his derriere.

The walls of the room were fair colored so as not to clutter and distract. Those close to him would say, however, that no external influences could ever affect his work ethic. Ever since grade school, his mother tells, Orpet was dedicated to hard work and success. The fourth of ten children, Orpet learned at a very early age that hard work was the only way to achieve success. Whether it was a bed, a pair of shoes or a meal, Orpet took nothing for granted.

Alarm clocks, among other things, were too few to go around and the now famous family story tells of how Orpet angrily lectured his mother one morning during his third year of grade school when she failed to wake him up on time, which caused him to be ten minutes late for the first bell.

"Don't you know if I'm late I can't get the award for perfect attendance at the awards assembly," he said with his jet black hair standing on end to the heights of the Sugarloaf in Rio de Janeiro and his hazel brown eyes bugging out halfway across the Botafogo Bay.

He then proceeded to lecture his mother on the merits of promptness and their relationship for future success. That same afternoon, Orpet gathered up some money he had saved from various chores and bought himself an alarm clock. Needless to say, his mother testifies, he was never late for school again.

Nor was he late for much else. Much like his first alarm clock, Orpet operated with extreme accuracy and perfection. Deadlines were met; assignments were completed and appointments were kept. Bills were always paid on time and in full, never to waste a penny on interest charges or penalties. His spending was frugal, and investments were shrewd. Most importantly, he let his actions always do the talking. Moving quietly, and often secretly, he never let words get in the way of what he wanted to do.

Among his mottoes: "A tree grows but makes no noise while doing so."

Orpet's career in the Brazilian Navy grew more rapidly than any tree. A straight-A student all through school and into his military training, Orpet placed himself at the very top of every class. He possessed an acutely sharp mathematical mind and he pursued and devoured every subject that he studied. His success as an engineer was matched by his success as a businessman which made him that much more valuable to the Navy.

He was transferred from Rio de Janeiro to a more significant post in São Paulo and he spent a great deal of time in the nuclear program of the University of São Paulo. He found himself called upon to serve in a variety of higher capacity and higher responsibility projects of the Navy, many of them highly secretive, which suited him well. As Brazil's quest for more advanced technology in the military increased, so did Orpet's duties. He was selected to attend Stanford University for a two-year study course. The purpose and scope of his program in the United States was in a league that few Brazilian engineers had ventured into. Having spent a lifetime of working hard and studying seriously, plus two years of the same at Stanford, Orpet returned home an accomplished, yet still very ambitious officer.

The phone rang and Orpet immediately set down the papers that he had been organizing on his desk and answered the phone.

"Hey Sergio, long time," he said, "I thought you'd forgotten about me."

He walked with the portable phone around the desk and towards the bay window. In the distance, he saw his eleven year old son swing smoothly and successfully at the golf ball that now sailed through the air. Orpet smiled proudly as he turned away from the window.

"Sergio, I want to make an offer on that piece of land out near the school but not until I get word about the developer's plans. You stay in touch with me about that every day, not once a week. It's timing, my friend."

Orpet sat down at his desk again and leafed through a newspaper as he continued on the phone.

"Let me know also if you hear anything new about that company in Sunnyvale that was in the Wall Street Journal the other day...What do you mean, 'that's risky?' You're supposed to tell me about guarantees, not risks, that's what I pay you for Sergio, guarantees."

Orpet continued on the phone for another ten minutes as he also plowed through the newspapers and mail on his desk. As his business in the office proceeded, Elida's picked up as well.

Her on again, off again art career began to gain momentum

with the completion of a series of oil paintings that had been displayed at a small art fair in a neighboring suburban community. One of the works, a delicate and fine pastel composition of a mother and daughter strolling with parasols in a field of flowers, brought an offer from a collector in São Paulo. He lost out, however, not because his offer was low, but because Elida had done the painting for Orpet's sister and husband who lived in Los Angeles. For the most part, her dabblings with brush and canvas were a non-profit venture anyway. Her real work, before the children were born, was in architecture.

She studied in school in Rio and had worked for a few years drawing blueprints for new homes and new projects in Rio, before putting it aside to begin drawing her family blueprint. Off and on she would paint but never anything too serious. As the children grew older, especially after returning from the United States, Elida began thinking more and more about work. Not long after Orpet began getting comfortable in his office, she moved her easel into a corner of the room. Soon after, a shelf went up to store some art supplies, followed by a small bookcase for her old college art books. If it weren't for the fact that this invasion had legitimate business implications, Orpet probably would have put his foot down. Instead, he supported his wife's work, and welcomed the new additions to his office.

He also, as was usually the case, had a master plan laid out. Two years before they moved to the United States, just a year after Paloma was born, they built a vacation house in Araras. Orpet's parents first ventured to this mountain retreat, one hour from Rio, many years before and built a modest house of their own. Nestled amongst rich, lush mountains covered with the greenest of vegetation, the house in Araras was the family's simple vacation hideaway. Stocked with gardens and a small chicken coop, it also served as a family grocery store of sorts, and a small business, as eggs and vegetables were brought down the mountain every week into the city.

Together with his sister and brother-in-law, who lived in Rio, Orpet purchased land in Araras less than a mile from his parents house, divided it and then turned it over to Elida when it came time to build. She designed every corner of both houses; one three-bedroom ranch house which sat on an elevated plateau and a two-story, three-bedroom house which sat on the lower portion of the land below. Both homes were simple, but they were extra special being that Elida had created them. As she spent many a sunny afternoon on her wooden deck of the two-story house, Elida maintained a great sense of accomplishment.

Orpet encouraged her to continue with her creativity. Although they were happy in their present house, it was not a permanent situation and they eagerly awaited the opportunity to purchase land and have Elida design a new home. She had so many ideas that were not feasible for the vacation house so she knew exactly what she wanted to do this time around. Orpet could sense the excitement and the inspiration in his wife as they talked over and over about the project. He also diligently studied the real estate market in search of the right land deal. As he got closer to making an offer on the land he wanted, he allowed Elida to move all of her easels and architectural materials into the office on a permanent basis.

Paloma passed by the office on her way down the hallway. She stopped at the door and then entered in a hurry, jumping right up on her father's lap. Orpet was often perplexed at Paloma's mood swings. One minute she'd be quiet or short with him or at times they would argue and he'd become strict to control her but without fail, at some point, she'd seemingly forget whatever had happened and jump up into his lap.

"Hi, Dad," she said with a huge smile. "What are you doing?"

Orpet lifted his head from the papers in front of him and smiled back at Paloma, sighting the opportunity to get even with his sagacious little daughter.

"Paloma, please, I already explained that to your Mom. Can you ask her?"

Unamused by her father's sagacity, Paloma jumped down from his lap and skipped towards the door. "Fine," she said with a smile as she headed out of the office.

Elida was standing over a pot of boiling water on the stove in the kitchen, when Paloma entered.

"What are you making Mom?" she asked as she walked right up to the hot stove. "May I help you?"

"I'd love for you to help Paloma," Elida answered as she stirred a pot of rice on a burner next to the water. I'm making rice and corn and there's a chicken in the fryer also. If you'd like, you can set the table."

Paloma took on the task with joy. The way she set the table showed a lot about her character and Elida watched proudly. She gently placed each item on the table at perfect angles. The napkins were folded at perfect angles as well. Everything was arranged delicately and beautifully. She finished the table by placing a floral arrangement from the living room near Elida's place setting.

"I'm gonna take a walk." she said to her mother after finishing.

"Alone?"

"Why not? I'm not afraid of anything."

"Just be careful, Paloma, and be back soon for lunch."

Paloma walked proudly out of the kitchen, through the sliding glass door and into the back yard. In the distance, halfway down the fairway of the third hole, Paloma spotted her brother working on a chip shot. She ran alongside the rough of the fairway, underneath the row of eucalyptus trees that bordered the fairway, and began calling out Tiago's name.

"Quiet." Tiago whispered as he lifted his head from the ball which sat up on the well manicured grass.

"How are you doing?" Paloma asked her brother as she trotted up to him from behind.

"How's the golfing?"

"It's fine Paloma," he answered patiently, "but you have to keep quiet on a golf course. It's what they call golf etiquette."

"Sounds important," she responded. "Let me see you hit it."

Tiago refocused his attention on the little white subject and placed his club gently behind it. Smoothly he dragged it back along the grass and then just as smoothly he brought it down through the ball. Paloma watched in admiration as the ball arched up into the air and carried within a few feet of the green.

"Great shot!" Paloma cheered as she raced after the ball. Before Tiago could teach his sister anything else about golf etiquette, Paloma picked up the ball and came running back towards Tiago.

"Do it again," Paloma said with a big smile.

Tiago took good care of his little sister. He was extremely patient with her and he loved her unconditionally, which was difficult at times considering her temper outbursts. Unlike with others though, Paloma rarely fought with Tiago. He was a sweet and docile boy who kept primarily to himself and rarely let the outside world interfere with his solitude. Friends of the family often said that Tiago lived in a world of his own. If so, it was a pleasant and peaceful world in which anyone would have liked to live.

Paloma looked up to Tiago fondly as she gave him the golf ball. He took it from her with equal amounts of disbelief and understanding.

"Thanks, Paloma. Now why don't you continue your walk towards the other fairway?"

Paloma obliged and went sprinting off in another direction. The winter's sun was warm and the grass underneath her sandals was soft and warm as well. She reduced her sprint to a leisurely skip and eventually to a slow walk as she left the fairway and crossed the road that led to the new housing development going up in the community. Paloma reached the side of the road that would soon be the front yard of one of the new houses. Dirt was scattered haphazardly about as the landscaping part of the construction had yet to begin. The major construction of the house was complete; as Paloma approached the front door, it looked like a perfectly fine house to her.

The front door was open so Paloma entered without hesitation. She waked curiously through the main living room which was bare from floor to ceiling. The smell of fresh paint flowed from the kitchen and as Paloma entered, she found several cans of open paint sitting on the floor. She browsed around the kitchen like an artist in a paint supply store. Uninterested in the large cans of white paint, Paloma's interest perked up considerably when she came across a small can of red paint and quite conveniently, a thin brush lying on the floor.

Wondering about Paloma's whereabouts, Elida finished preparing lunch just as Renata came home.

Closely resembling the characteristics of her father, Renata was dedicated and committed to everything she did. Slender and prettier than most of her thirteen-year-old friends, Renata showed a presence of success and stature. She had a bright and intelligent mind that propelled her self-motivation and confidence. Somewhat unlike her father and other members of the family, however, Renata possessed an exotic and flamboyant personality that made her the life of every party. Her spot as the most popular student in the high school yearbook could have been reserved as early as kindergarten.

"Why did you fry the chicken Mom?" Renata asked. "I thought that you were watching cholesterol?"

"You're right. I shouldn't have fried it, but it's fast and today fast is important."

"Where are you going so fast?" Renata continued her interrogation as she removed serving dishes from the cupboard.

"Out with your father, later, but if I don't find time to rest in the afternoon, I'll be a zombie. Can you take care of cleanup after lunch and then find something quiet to entertain Paloma so that I can nap?"

"Quiet? Paloma? Do you think it's possible Mom?"

"Renata, don't say those things about your sister."

For the moment, Paloma was quite entertained. She stood in the living room of the formerly perfectly clean new house. With the small can of red paint between her feet and the brush firmly in her hand, Paloma was happily in the middle of a painting extravaganza. The base of one wall was streaked with red lines, apparently where Paloma had initially tested her materials.

A few feet off of the floor on the wall to the rear, Paloma's true artistry had begun taking form. Scattered about were little red hearts and beneath the group of half dozen or so hearts was Paloma's name, printed neatly in red paint. Apparently satisfied with her work, Paloma picked up the can of paint and wandered out of the living room. She passed through a small corridor and into the adjacent room.

Tiago entered the garage and threw his golf clubs into the golf bag which was hanging on a nail. He kicked off his sneakers which were stained with the bright green of the fairway's fresh grass. In his formerly white socks, he ran around the house to the back where Wolf was temporarily locked up.

"Dad, did you feed Wolf yet?" Tiago shouted through the sliding glass door to the kitchen.

"No, go ahead," Orpet replied as he stood in the kitchen pouring the drinks for lunch. "Feed him and then come in and wash up for lunch."

Just as Orpet was about to ask Elida the whereabouts of Paloma, the telephone rang. Orpet finished pouring his own drink and then picked up the phone.

"Hello. ... Yes, what's up...my daughter?"

Elida dropped a serving spoon on the table and knocked over the salt shaker in the process. "Oh, my God!" she shrieked as she moved towards Orpet.

"I'll be right there," Orpet said calmly into the phone.

"Orpet, what happened?" Elida inquired not so calmly.

"Calm down, it's nothing serious. It was one of the security guards. Paloma's down the street at one of the new houses. She's into some kind of mess but she's all right."

Elida raced ahead of everyone towards the front door.

"She's a rascal," Renata blurted out as she closed the door behind her and followed the rest of the family down the street.

Paloma stood quietly in the living room of the new house with the unwelcome company of the security guard. Elida entered first, followed in order by Tiago, Renata, and Orpet. They all froze in their tracks as soon as they saw the walls. There was a long silence as everyone looked around in disbelief. The quiet and intense perusing was reminiscent of an art gallery but the security guard, among others, had no intention of seeing art galleries built in the community.

"Have the Association give me a call and I'll deal with it later," Orpet told the security guard rather frankly. He then took Paloma by the hand and walked out of the house.

"Wow! This is unbelievable!" Tiago said as he walked around the room.

"Let's go kids," Orpet yelled back.

"Don't you want to take any pictures of this?" Renata asked with a sarcastic smile.

"Let's go!" Orpet answered.

Outside, Orpet and Paloma walked over the dirt, holding hands. Orpet was not visibly angry but he certainly wasn't smiling either. Paloma was quiet.

"So you like to paint, huh, Paloma?"

Paloma nodded her head but did not look at her father nor say a word.

"Other people's houses?" Orpet continued.

Paloma shrugged her shoulders, but remained silent.

"I don't know about you sometimes Paloma."

Inside the house, Tiago and Renata continued admiring the work of their sister. Unamused, the security guard began picking up the cans of paint and the brushes. Elida walked slowly around the living room and then passed through the corridor to the adjacent room.

She saw a few more hearts and flowers splattered on the walls but as she walked in the direction of the window on the rear wall, her eyes were drawn to a small arrangement of red paint. As she got closer, the words and figures that had been so carefully crafted with the paint brush upon the wall became clearer. Elida read them to herself:

"Mommy I
love you
A kiss, Paloma"

Elida dropped to her knees on the bare floor and brought her eyes closer to the wall. She remained frozen on the floor for what seemed to her like a lifetime. Suddenly, the impatient voice of the security guard jolted her to her feet.

"Ma'am, I'm going to lock up the house now," the guard said.

Elida looked at the man but didn't respond with any words. She slowly lifted herself off of the floor and walked silently out of the house.

Chapter 4

Paloma was born on June 11th, 1981.

For those who seek their reasons in astrology, this date would explain Paloma's personality. She was indeed a Gemini. She was sweet and tender and loving while her twin, who would appear on a moment's notice, was temperamental and abrasive and combative. She was also very independent, and often quite lonely. She was impeccably clean and organized, very straightforward with her wishes and desires and she never, ever lied.

Auxiliadora knew this all very well. She was as close to Paloma as anyone outside of the immediate family. Auxiliadora was the maid. Now a maid in Brazil is quite different than a maid in Beverly Hills. Most middle-class Brazilian families have maids to do the basic chores of the house and take care of the children. But beyond that, due primarily to the nature of the Brazilian family, the maid becomes part of the family. Auxiliadora was a part of the family long before Paloma came along.

On Rua Campos Sales in Tijuca, when Lourdes gave birth to her fourth child, Orpet Jr., Auxiliadora was there to take care of the boy. She worked for Lourdes in that busy, bustling house and she saw many of the children grow. Her life, as it so often does, went in other directions until some thirty years later when she landed another job as a maid, this time in a small apartment in São Paulo.

The woman she worked for was named Elida, coincidentally, if you happen to believe in coincidences. It wasn't until she went to hang some piece of clothing in a closet one day that Auxiliadora found out who the man of the house was. As she reached for a hanger, a wooden hanger that men used in the Navy, she saw a name written in bold letters on it: Orpet.

"Funny," she said to Elida, "I worked many, many years ago in a house in Rio that had a father and a son with this name."

And so it was that Auxiliadora came to be part of the family that saw Orpet born and then Paloma born.

Auxiliadora loved to cook and Paloma loved it when she baked a chocolate cake. The two would laugh and giggle and carry on from dawn till dusk in that little apartment in São Paulo. Auxiliadora was the perfect playmate for Paloma and they loved each other dearly.

Life went in other directions once again and this time Auxiliadora did not follow. Paloma was three years old, Tiago was seven, and Renata was nine when Orpet accepted the Navy's assignment at Stanford University.

Much like Rio de Janeiro and many other areas of Brazil, the San Francisco Bay area is a fascinating and majestic combination of ocean and bays, seaports and fishing boats, bridges and islands, mountains and hillsides, city life and exotic culture. And so it was with great excitement and anticipation that the family moved to Northern California.

Orpet went ahead of the rest of the family and rented a house in Menlo Park. A few months later when he got familiar with the price of housing in California, he moved to a town house next to campus.

Life in California was terrific. Although Orpet studied seriously day and night, there was some time made for diversions. There were trips to the snow in Lake Tahoe and a first attempt at skiing. There were long drives down the Pacific Coast Highway to Los Angeles and San Diego and visits to Disneyland and Sea World. And there was shopping, a lot of shopping.

Brazilians love to shop as it is, but when the Navy is eventually moving you home and ushering you past customs with ease, the desire to shop for the latest and finest appliances and electronics is increased. And so it was in mall after mall, after mall.

As children so easily do, Renata, Tiago and for the most part, Paloma, adapted to their new home. They did well in school, they made friends and they got involved in the activities of American life. Tiago even learned about football, the kind only Americans play, and he cheered the 49ers in the Super Bowl.

Being the youngest and being the temperamental little Gemini that she was, Paloma was slower to adapt. In a supermarket she screamed and covered her ears in horror when a woman spoke English to her. Later, of course, she would refuse to speak Portuguese and speak only English.

She did not have many friends and that was troubling to her. She wanted to have friends, but she just didn't, except for Kamilah.

Paloma's friend Kamilah was black, like Auxiliadora, but not really, at least not to Paloma. She was brown, actually. After Kamilah had moved away, prior to Paloma moving back to Brazil, the two exchanged letters. One day Paloma received a picture of her friend. She showed the picture with great joy and pride to some other children.

"But she's black," the others responded when seeing the picture.

"Not black!" Paloma screamed in anger. "Brown!"

Paloma raced home as furious and hurt as could be and fighting back tears she recounted the incident to her mother. Elida advised her to go back to the children and ask them if they knew the color of Kamilah inside. Paloma took the advice and went back to the children. Elida never knew exactly what Paloma told those children but she did return to the house quite satisfied and clutching tightly in the palm of her hand the picture of her dear, brown friend.

Kamilah liked Paloma in spite of her. Paloma was often strong and authoritative but Kamilah accepted Paloma's ways in a tender manner. She understood and forgave Paloma for her occasional outbursts of temper. She spent more time appreciating the good times than the bad and Paloma loved her for that.

Both Lourdes and Dora came to visit in the Bay Area, which enabled Orpet and Elida to have an extra babysitter and an opportunity to spend some time alone. Orpet was not particularly fond of making the drive to San Francisco because he usually had an abundance of studying to do and would prefer a shorter night out close to home. But, when it came time to treating his wife to fresh seafood, he made the drive with no complaints.

On a quiet cul-de-sac not far from Fisherman's Wharf, squeezed between a flower shop and a small art gallery, stood a fragile wooden building that no one would recognize as an eatery were it not for the smell of freshly baked sourdough bread which seeped out from under the front door. Elida first got a whiff of the bread on her first trip into the city when she picked up a frame at the art gallery. She had stopped for what she thought would be a quick bowl of chowder. Instead she had a virtual religious experience that she grew more fond of each time.

The restaurant's owner and lone chef, a crusty old New Englander, baked his sourdough bread into the shape of the bowls and then filled the bowls with his own steaming seafood chowder; a concoction of shrimp, clams, mussels and hearty chunks of fresh halibut and cod. That, along with a cold glass of California Chardonnay, was usually enough for Elida.

Other times, it was shrimp, just shrimp. Elida loved shrimp. Orpet would venture out and try oysters Rockefeller, clams casino, mesquite broiled New Zealand orange roughy and Cajun style blackened swordfish. Elida would eat shrimp; be it fried or broiled or barbecued or sauteed, Elida would eat shrimp.

Before they had even crossed the city limits, Elida knew where they were going but she stayed silent not to spoil her husband's well-intentioned surprise. As they made their way past the Wharf at Pier 39, she leaned over and kissed him on the cheek.

"Hungry? I know a place." Orpet said.

"You know all the right places, don't you?"

They sat at a small booth in no particular area of the restaurant. They shared a bottle of wine, a Caesar salad and shrimp cocktail. Orpet then had poached Alaskan Salmon and Elida had more shrimp. The evening was as mellow as the food was delicious. Afterwards, they walked briefly by the waterside, Orpet placing his arm around Elida to shield off the cool nighttime breeze. A dinner ferry pulled into dock, unloading an elderly group of tourists. Orpet saw an old man and he thought of his father and the times they spent by the water and the beaches in Rio. Back then he had to ask his father to go to the beach. He no longer had to ask to get the things he wanted. He was in complete control now.

The drive home from San Francisco was more pleasant than Orpet had anticipated. He held Elida's hand most of the way and with the help of an easy listening radio station that hummed through the stereo system of the car he leased, they were home in no time.

The house was dark and silent as Orpet and Elida entered. Dora had fallen asleep on the couch of the living room but she woke up as the kitchen light went on. Orpet poured himself a glass of mineral water in the kitchen as Elida helped her mother to the bedroom. He opened the blinds to the sliding glass door and turned on the outside light. He noticed in the distance, out in the common grass area of the town house development, Paloma's bicycle. He left the light on a minute while pondering whether or not to go outside and get it.

Elida entered the kitchen with Paloma which immediately

irritated Orpet.

"What the heck is this?" he exclaimed. "You should be in bed."

"I couldn't sleep, Mom," Paloma said, virtually ignoring her father.

"Get one glass of water fast and go to bed," Elida said.

"Paloma," Orpet continued in an irritated voice "did you know that you left your bicycle outside in the grass?"

"Oh no, I thought I organized everything," she said.

She walked with her glass of water to the sliding glass door to take a look. She then put the glass on the floor and began opening the door.

"What are you doing?" Orpet asked.

"Paloma, you can get it in the morning," Elida jumped in.

"No, I have to get it now."

Orpet walked out of the kitchen, disgusted by the whole thing. Elida walked to the door as Paloma stepped outside.

"But it's dark Paloma."

"I'm not afraid of the dark. I'm not afraid of anything."

Elida was not at ease with that. Paloma had shown a bold spirit before and now, at four and a half, she seemed to be even bolder. Elida watched in disbelief as Paloma ran across the grass in the dark night. Her heart skipped a few beats but she realized that indeed, there wasn't anything to worry about. The night was calm, the area was safe and Elida could see Paloma very clearly as she made her way towards the bike. Finally, a bright smile came to her face as Paloma came back towards the house with the bike. Paloma was smiling too. Orpet, who returned to the kitchen to put his glass in the sink, was not smiling at all.

A few months later, after nearly two full years of living in California, no one was smiling when the movers came to pack and ship everything back to Brazil. Orpet had finished, successfully once again, his work at Stanford and the Navy needed him back in São Paulo. It was time to pack away fond memories and good experiences and re-adapt to a new life. Renata took back a handful of swimming trophies, Tiago took back his 49ers jersey and Paloma took back her picture of Kamilah. The three of them also took back a fluency in English which could carry them far in Brazil.

Orpet took back a great deal of knowledge acquired at Stanford and he also made a few notches in his belt in terms of being an accomplished world traveler. As for Elida, she would say, as so many do, that she left her heart in San Francisco. Funny song. It would be her heart, more than anything, which she would need as she resumed her life in Brazil.

Chapter 5

After having spent Christmas in the snow in Northern California, Christmas in Brazil had never been the same in the years that followed. Memories of chilly days and snow covered mountain tops in Lake Tahoe were far away as the temperature in São Paulo reached 100 degrees and the only white seen was in the sand on the beach.

Christmas would also never be the same for Elida because it was on December 25th that her father passed away. It was sudden and it was unexpected and for Elida it made the routine of Christmas a bittersweet task. As the warm December sun had set on Christmas Eve, she tried her best to be festive, mostly for the children. She wrapped presents with Renata and let Paloma do the ribbons. They also packed for the trip to Rio where Christmas would be celebrated at Lourdes' house on Rua Campos Sales.

"Elida," Orpet called out from the office, "can you come here?"

"I'll be right there," she said as she held her finger tightly over the ribbon as Paloma tried to make a knot.

"Elida, what is this $36.00 charge on the credit card bill for?" he asked as she walked into the office. "The name of the store is here but I can't find a receipt."

"Orpet, why are you paying bills on Christmas Eve?"

"Why? Because I don't think Santa Claus is going to pay them for me, that's why."

"He might if you've been good this year," she said as she walked behind the desk to look at the bill in question.

"Very funny. The charge is right here," he pointed, "and there's no receipt. How many times have I told you to save the receipts?"

"It must be around somewhere. I can look for it, but not now."

"Just put all your receipts in this envelope and we won't have this problem. How difficult can that be?"

"It's not a problem, Orpet." Elida said as she walked away from the desk. "Just lighten up. It's Christmas Eve, you know, joyous day."

"Yea, fine; one other thing. I have a bill for Tiago's swimming lessons, two sessions a week. How come I haven't seen him go this week?"

"I didn't take him this week."

"Why not?"

"I just didn't; he didn't mind."

"Wait a second. I'm paying for swimming lessons that he's not going to. That's beautiful, really beautiful."

"He'll go next week Orpet."

"That's not the point...."

"Forget it Orpet," Elida snapped back. "He'll go next week. Just pay the damn bill."

Elida stormed out of the office and Orpet got up and followed after her. Paloma walked down the hallway and stepped between them.

"Stop fighting on Christmas!" Paloma said authoritatively.

The mood was a bit more joyous on Christmas Day as Orpet packed the car and got the family together.

"Is everybody happy?"

Though the sentiment was sincere, the line had become sort of a family joke. As a matter of routine, the affairs of the family when traveling could not proceed until Orpet had the confirmation that everybody was in the proper spirit. Occasionally, in response to the question, someone would lodge a minor complaint, but most often, to preserve the tradition, everyone would answer with a joyful affirmative.

As Orpet pulled the station wagon out of the driveway and headed down the road in Lago Azul, a collective "yes" was echoed from the back seat to the question and even Elida managed a smile and a positive nod of her head. The drive from São Paulo to Rio was about six hours long and they had made the drive so many times that it was routine. They left early enough to get to Dora's apartment in the afternoon for a visit and lunch with her, and with Elida's brother and sister. Dinner, and a more complicated–in Elida's opinion–Christmas party at Lourdes' house would be that night.

The conversation in the car centered mainly on Elida's father and how improbable it was that he had died exactly on Christmas Day. Elida vividly remembered the details of that day as did the children, especially Renata, who comforted her mother and grandmother all day.

"Do you think Grandpa's in heaven now?" Paloma asked no one in particular.

"I pray that he is," Elida answered.

"What if there is no heaven?" Tiago spoke up. "What if when you die you just rot in the ground and get eaten by bugs?"

"That's sick, Tiago," Renata said.

"Well, maybe it's true," he said. "What do you think Dad?"

"I'm not so sure," Orpet said as he concentrated more on the road than the conversation. "I guess the most amazing thing about dying is that you don't know what happens to you until it happens, and there is no way to know before. Think about it. Think about all the things that you can know. Think about all the books that you can read, all the computers that you can work with. No matter how much you learn the one subject you'll never get to learn about is what happens to you when you die."

"That makes us all equal," Renata said, following her father's idea and agreeing with it. "That makes us all equally ignorant."

"I'm not ignorant," Paloma said.

"I didn't say you were, rascal," Renata said with a laugh, "I just said that we're all like Dad said we were and that's the way it is."

"But I'm not ignorant," Paloma said.

The conversation shifted to the family and a quiz to see if the children could name all the brothers and sisters and their children on Orpet's side. There were ten brothers and sisters and a present total of seventeen children and to the surprise of Orpet, everyone, including Paloma, could name them off without error. Renata even correctly placed the ages of all the children. By the time she had finished, they had arrived in Rio.

The city was more crowded than it was on their last visit. It had more people, more cars, more noise and more trash each and every year. It was still beautiful, Orpet noted, as they drove around the Botafogo Bay and watched the cable car climb to the top of the Sugarloaf, but as is the case with everything and everybody, time was getting the best of Rio de Janeiro.

The afternoon at Dora's was pleasant and cheerful despite a few moments when Elida's father's name came up. Dora, who seemed to be the most cheerful, served an assortment of Brazilian appetizers and a potato salad while Orpet mixed some drinks. They sat and ate and drank and talked until almost eight p.m., at which time Orpet reminded Elida, and then insisted, that they leave for his mother's house.

A family gathering at Rua Campos Sales was not exactly a walk in the park for Elida. With an aging widow, ten grown brothers and sisters, a half dozen or so spouses plus a full soccer team of children, the household was already a soap opera in progress, and Elida was as much a part of it as anyone. There were the typical on-going family political matters, there was some residue left over from incidents in the past, there was one still not talking to another for some reason and there were petty jealousies about jobs or houses or children.

Still, there was also a great deal of genuine love in the family that Christmas Day. Lourdes had made a lavish meal with her famous shrimp empadas, rice, black beans, grilled sausage, a turkey, and loads of trimmings. There was plenty of beer and wine and harder stuff for those who wanted, or needed. For dessert there were fruit cakes and flan and ice cream, plus freshly brewed coffee and liqueurs.

The children had full run of the house although its aging floors creaked with every twist and turn they made. They played, or banged the old piano and teased the two German Shepherds who were kept locked up on the outside veranda.

Elida leaned against a bookshelf with a glass of wine in her hand and talked with a sister-in-law, forming one of several cliques that had clearly developed in the house.

"The kids are fine," she said, "I suppose."

"What do you mean?."

"Oh, I don't know, I suppose that I think too much."

"About what?"

"About Paloma. It's hard to explain and even harder to understand. She's so complex. I mean Renata and Tiago seem so simple. They're both easy-going, good natured, never making waves. They both do well in school, they're into their friends and their activities. They seem content. But Paloma seems agitated at times. She has the darndest temper tantrums like you can't believe. You've witnessed them. Most of the time, especially when she's with me, she's so warm and fun-loving, but when she's among others, her mood changes. It's as if an entirely different personality was entering her body. It's kind of scary."

"Paloma's comfortable around you, that's good. She just hasn't reached the level of comfort with others yet. That'll come. It's all part of maturing. She's only what, seven and a half?"

"Yea, seven and a half, but it's not just that. It's as if she's being bothered by something. Her mood changes are definitely connected to something that's going on within her or around her, but it's never when she's with me."

"How's she doing in school?"

"She's fine. She loves school and she loves her art. She comes home from school so excited to show me her drawings. Like I said, around me she's great. I don't know, maybe I'm just being naive and seeing more than there actually is."

"What does Orpet say?"

"You know him; he doesn't say much. He gets tough with her when she misbehaves but it doesn't last long. She responds through love and understanding, not toughness. She's just different, that's all. I don't worry, I just want her to grow up properly, to be happy, that's all. And while Orpet is tough on her, I seem to be too easy. I just can't bring myself to discipline her because, like I said, with me she's always fine."

"You just have to be patient, Elida. She's so young. She just needs time to grow and learn to express herself more maturely. You know me, I'm a screamer myself and I have a temper too. Heck, just ask Lourdes. No better not, it's Christmas. Let's leave well enough alone. Anyway I think that it's a lot healthier to open your mouth and say what's on your mind than to bottle it up and be quiet. Paloma just has a lot on her mind. She's bright and intelligent and she obviously knows what she wants and she's not afraid to let that be known. That's healthy. Let her be. With time she'll learn to focus all that energy in a positive way."

"You think so?"

"Sure. Forget it, let's have some more wine."

The two walked across the dining room and into the kitchen where Orpet sat talking with his brother. Elida helped herself to the bottle of wine that the men ignored since they preferred the bottle of scotch.

"Hey you, Mrs. Architect," Elida's brother-in-law said jokingly, "I didn't know you guys finally bought some land to build your house."

"Well, you know your secretive brother."

"Yea, I have to read the newspapers to keep up with how he's doing. So, what kind of house do you have planned?"

"Oh, we'll see," Elida replied as she headed out of the kitchen, being just as secretive as her husband.

"It's basically all hers," Orpet explained to his brother. "She's got the design planned out. I'll get involved only when construction starts. The tough part is staying on top of the contractors and that's where I'll step in. I'm not concerned about where the bedrooms are or what kind of handles we have on the sinks. I'll just watch the contractors and their invoices."

Renata and her teenage cousin walked into the kitchen and each grabbed a soda. Tall, slender, and very attractive, the pair stayed together the entire evening and caught up on everything there was to discuss about teenage life in São Paulo versus Rio.

"She's a good kid," Orpet said to his brother as he poured some more scotch and added a few ice cubes. "She really is. She's very smart and capable. Tiago too, he's the same way."

"And...."

"And what?"

"And Paloma?"

"Paloma's a different story."

"What do you mean?"

"It's hard to explain. She's not an easy child by any means. She has an unusual personality and many people, myself included, have some difficulty relating to her. But that doesn't worry me. Paloma has her own type of intelligence. She perceives things in a way that few children can. That will carry her far. You mark my word, this little girl, despite what others may think, is going to win big in this life."

"Who's going to win what?" Elida asked as she came back into the kitchen.

"Never mind," Orpet said, standing up and stretching.

"What's going on in the dining room Elida?"

"Same old, you know."

Orpet took his wife by the hand and walked into the dining room where Lourdes worked diligently at serving the desserts to the younger grandchildren. The older ones played in the back two bedrooms while an even older group sat on the steps downstairs and talked privately. Just as Orpet was about to help himself to some dessert, a few faint cross words echoed from the bedroom followed by an all too familiar high-pitched scream. Orpet immediately darted for the bedroom.

"Orpet, please," Elida tried to warn him, "take it easy."

"What was that?" one of the adults asked from the kitchen. "Who's screaming?"

"Who do you think?" another said. "It must be Paloma."

Elida overheard the comment, but refrained from commenting back. Instead, she pretended not to hear, turned her head, and walked away.

"What's going on in here?" Orpet bellowed as he entered the bedroom, the very bedroom that he had grown up in.

Paloma stood in the corner like a stone statue with her arms folded across her chest while her cousin sat on the floor, crying softly and kicking angrily some toys that were spread about the room.

"I'm not playing with her anymore!" Paloma lashed out. "These kids can't keep anything organized. It's a mess here. I want to go to my house now!"

"Oh, you'll go all right," her father lashed back. "You'll go home now and never go anywhere again."

"Yes I will," Paloma said with her arms still folded.

"What did you say, young lady?"

"I said I will," Paloma repeated loudly.

"You help clean up, Paloma."

"No!" she said firmly.

Paloma looked at her father but didn't say another word. Orpet's patience level dropped to its bottom. He stormed over to Paloma, grabbed her by the arm and dragged her to the middle of the room. Paloma's screams vibrated throughout the house.

"When this room is cleaned up and you apologize, Paloma, you come into the dining room together with your cousins and have some dessert. Do it, now."

"What happened?" Elida asked Orpet as she met him in the dining room.

"All part of the program," he said to her and the others as he calmly began serving his dessert again.

"I know Paloma's got a temper dear, but you've got to take it easy on her sometimes," Elida whispered to Orpet semi-privately.

"Take it easy?"

"Yes, you shouldn't have hit her."

"Hit her? I didn't hit her. Listen Elida, Paloma will learn to be patient and control her temper. I do not need to be taught or told how to act. She does. May I please have some whipped cream?"

"I just don't like it Orpet."

"I just don't want to talk about it anymore Elida."

Orpet sat at the end of the dining room table as a calming silence had settled over the room. Lourdes encouraged everyone to help themselves to dessert in order to get past the scene that had taken place. Within a matter of ten minutes, Paloma entered the dining room and diplomatically approached the table. She then strategically positioned herself alongside Orpet's left leg. He instinctively placed his coffee cup down and lifted Paloma onto his lap.

Showing a hint of regret for his confrontation with Paloma, Orpet decided as Paloma had already done, to simply forget the incident.

"What do you want for dessert Paloma?" he asked.

"Whatever you're having Dad."

"Let me serve you," Lourdes offered. "Do you want

whipped cream?"

"Yes, please," she answered politely and sweetly, with not a trace of anger or agitation to be seen.

Chapter 6

The sky was a near perfect azure blue which was typical for springtime in Brazil. A few puffy clouds dangled above, but nothing that could hide the brilliant sun that shone with generous warmth.

In the middle of the courtyard, absorbing those affectionate rays, stood a most majestic tree. Actually, calling it a tree would serve as an injustice. It was a complicated and fascinating sculpture of branches, twisting and tangling away from a proud and stalwart trunk.

A young boy could climb and wander unbridled throughout this maze of divergent limbs while a bluebird could just as easily find peace and solitude just resting amongst the outstretched and welcome arms, provided of course, that the boy was not present. For the moment, however, the only occupant was a warm breeze that passed in and out, gently tossing the leaves as it went.

Scattered at the base, somewhat deprived of the sun's rays, but healthy and vibrant nonetheless, were the most delicate roses. Their colors intertwined like a perfectly knitted quilt with alternating rows of red, yellow, pink and white. The other plants that resided in the courtyard did so with a reverence for the pulchritudinous flowers.

The courtyard was evenly paved with freshly laid red bricks, outlined by a shining strip of white paint, both of which contrasted greatly with the elderly patriarch which grew from the center. The contrasts of age, shape, space, color and form had come together to create an idyllic and halcyon little corner of the world.

Elida put some finishing touches on one of the roses as the hands of the wall clock in the office inched towards three. She had been working on the painting since noon on this particular sitting, three months since its initial inception. Two or three more sittings were all that Elida anticipated for its completion at which point the process of deciding where the painting would reside could begin.

Paloma's bus arrived at 3:10 so Elida quickly rinsed off her brush and hastily headed out of the door. The bus stop was only 200 yards from the house, but Elida moved swiftly to avoid being late. Paloma was not fond of riding the bus home from school. So on days when she couldn't make the 15 minute drive to the school to pick Paloma up, she certainly did not want to further upset things by being late at the bus stop.

The golden mini-bus passed through the gate which Salvador had opened as Elida stood talking to a neighbor about the new clubhouse being built at the pool. The bus was just about half the size of a normal school bus, providing service for the children of the enclosed community and one neighboring community. It puttered past the lake when Elida first got a glimpse of it and then slowly came to a stop as she waited anxiously to see her daughter.

Routinely, Paloma was the first to get off the bus. As the doors swung open, sure enough, Paloma hustled down the steps ahead of the others. By the looks of her smile and overall mood, Elida could tell that she had had a good day at school. Paloma had struggled a bit through first grade, allowing her temper to get in the way of her honest effort to do good work, but she was progressing in a more positive direction in her second year thanks in part to an extremely caring and patient teacher.

"What have you got?" Elida asked in reference to Paloma's overly stuffed backpack.

"Mom, I have so many pictures to show you. Today was art

day and I did a lot of work."

"That's funny. Today was art day for me, also. I did a lot of work on my painting. It's almost finished. Why don't we go home and look at each other's work?"

"Great idea," Paloma beamed.

As the congregation of parents and children at the bus stop dispersed, Elida and Paloma walked hand in hand down the road towards home. The sun was shining brightly even though it had rained just one hour before, a common weather pattern for April in Brazil. Paloma skipped past several small puddles which remained and Elida kept pace with a skip of her own. As the two neared the house, Renata raced past on her bicycle; she shouted as she rode by that she was on her way to a friend's house. Now fourteen years old, Renata seemed to live more and more at the houses of friends than at her own home.

"Be back by 4:00," Elida called out patiently, realizing more each day that patience was the only way to deal with a teenager. "Early dinner tonight, and I'll need your help, please."

Tiago, twelve years old and not yet at the craving for friends stage, sat alone on the living room couch. With one eye he read from his Brazilian history book, and with the other eye, he glanced at the television.

"Turn off the TV when you're doing homework, Tiago," Elida said as she entered the house with Paloma. "You know better than that."

"I'm not doing homework, Mom, I'm just watching TV."

"Very funny," Elida replied as she made her way into the kitchen. "Tiago, where are the chocolate chip cookies that I left on top of the refrigerator? I'm sure you may have seen them."

"Actually I did see them, Mom. They were pretty good."

"Tiago!" Elida screeched out, "you know, if your father were here he'd make you find a way to get those cookies back on top of the refrigerator."

Orpet wasn't home, and wouldn't be for some time, so the

cookie incident ended there. Orpet was involved with much more than cookies as the Navy had sent him to Europe for a conference on nuclear research and testing.

"Mom, let's go look at the drawings," Paloma insisted as Elida poked around the kitchen. "Forget the cookies, Mom; just come with me to look at the drawings."

"Yea, Mom," Tiago said sarcastically from the living room, "forget about the cookies and go look at the drawings."

"You run ahead, Paloma. I have to look for something else for our dessert tonight, something we can have while Tiago is doing the dishes."

"I heard that." Tiago shouted back.

"You were supposed to hear it. Tiago, dinner at 4:00, O.K.? You and Renata have church classes at 5:00 and Paloma has dance class. Let's be on time."

"Renata is not here, you know. She went to Allison's house."

"I know. I saw her on the bike. She'll be home on time."

Elida walked down the hallway and into the office where Paloma was seated at her mother's easel. She gazed fondly at her mother's canvas.

"This is so beautiful, Mommy. What are you going to call it?"

"I'm not sure yet. What do you think?"

"How about...how about...Oh, I can't think."

"That's all right, Paloma; let it be. Art has a way of eventually sinking into you. We'll keep looking at it, feeling it, and a name will come along. A name will fall from the tree just like a leaf does."

"Look at my drawings, Mom," Paloma said as she opened her folder. "This flower drawing I did with crayons, but I should have used markers. I can't draw roses like you can so I guess it doesn't matter."

"But Paloma, you..."

"This," Paloma continued excitedly, "this is the book that I finished illustrating."

"Wolf's Adventures?"

"Yea, it's a book about Wolf. Look, here he is in the back-yard and here he is with Tiago."

"That's Tiago?"

"Sure. See the blue sneakers? That's him. And look at this. This is Wolf barking at the ducks at the lake. Funny, huh?"

"Very funny, and very good too."

Paloma continued describing the details of her book but Elida's eyes had moved to the folder where she saw a yellow piece of paper with a strikingly impressive sketch.

"What's this one?" Elida asked.

"That's special, Mom." Paloma shyly tucked the paper away and didn't say another word.

"Paloma, this is so beautiful. You did this?"

"I did, Mom."

"But I never knew you could draw something so lovely and so special.."

"I told you Mom, I'm going to be an artist."

"You're already an artist, Paloma."

At precisely 5:00, Tiago entered the main classroom of the Holy Angels Church and respectfully greeted his teacher, Mrs. Santiago. Mrs. Santiago, a refined lady with distinctively bold, dark eyes, and solid gray hair, was a liberal Catholic thinker who taught religion by allowing her children to freely express their curiosities and necessities rather than telling them what those curiosities and necessities should be.

Renata sat at the front of the class in the small, windowless room that was carved out of the back wing of the Holy Angels Church. It was a modernistic building that was totally void of all the historical and deeply religious representations that give most of the churches in Brazil their presence.

Orpet and Elida liked the church for its liberal and contemporary slant and they contributed to its financial upkeep when they could, or rather, when they decided to. They did not attend Mass too regularly which troubled Elida in terms of the hypocritical message it sent to the children, but nothing was ever done about it. Renata and Tiago continued with their religious education. Paloma did not.

In the evening, Renata and Tiago worked independently on their respective school and church homework assignments. Alone in her bedroom, Paloma did her school homework neatly and swiftly. She then organized her many school books and papers in the drawers of her desk and pulled out a clean, lined white piece of paper.

Elida stopped in the hallway just outside Paloma's bedroom.

"It's almost lights out Paloma, finish up."

"Mom, am I going to church school when I get older?" Paloma asked as she covered up the paper that she had been writing on.

"Yes, absolutely. Would you like to pray with me before you go to sleep?" Elida asked.

"No," Paloma answered so bluntly that Elida was shocked.

"Well, O.K.," Elida said after a pause, "you're not going to pray but I am."

Elida entered her bedroom and before praying, she filled the tub with hot water and bath oil. She removed her clothes and placed them on a towel rack. Before entering the bath, she placed the phone near the tub as Orpet would be calling from Europe, as he did once a day.

Elida relaxed in the tub for nearly thirty minutes as she spoke to Orpet on the phone. When she opened the bathroom door to hang the phone up, she literally stepped on a piece of paper that sat rather strategically on the floor just outside the bathroom. She carefully straightened it out and sat upon the bed to read it.

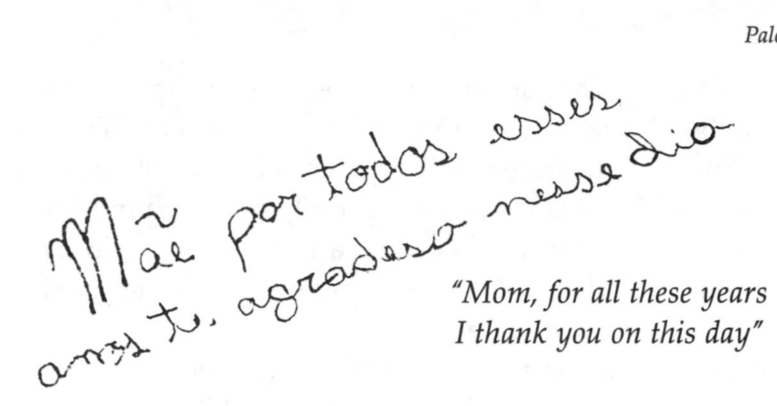

"Mom, for all these years
I thank you on this day"

E- esperança
L- loucura
I- inspiração
D- doçura
A- amor

"hope"
"madness"
"inspiration"
"sweetness"
"love"

O teu nome estára gravado
com migo até o fim da vida

"Your name will be engraved in
me until the end of life"

Elida remained motionless on the bed, admiring the stunning beauty of the words and thoughts that Paloma had written. She read the note over and over before finally getting to her feet. With the note tucked securely in the palm of her hand, she walked out of the bedroom and down the hallway.

"Are you sleeping?" Elida whispered to Paloma as she poked her head inside the bedroom.

"Not really." Paloma answered into the darkness.

"Come into my bed for a while Paloma," Elida suggested happily as she helped Paloma out from under the covers.

As the two walked towards the master bedroom, Elida began asking about the note, but Paloma didn't utter a word. They got into bed and Elida continued asking, tenderly and curiously, why and how she had written such a beautiful note, but mysteriously, to Elida, Paloma didn't answer.

"I'm going to pray," Elida told Paloma as she tucked the covers up under her chin. "Would you like to pray now?"

"No," Paloma answered again.

"Very well," Elida answered just as bluntly, and she began to pray out loud "Our Father, who art in heaven, hallowed be thy name..."

"Pray to yourself," Paloma interrupted, bluntly but politely.

Elida continued praying in the same tone, hoping that Paloma would join in, but she didn't.

Chapter 7

"Make my room big," Renata said to Elida as she poked her head into the office where Elida sat diligently drawing the fine lines of the blueprint. "And make sure there is at least one telephone jack and at least five electrical outlets."

"What do you need five electrical outlets for?"

"One for my blow dryer, one for my stereo, one for my TV, one for my computer, and one extra for emergencies."

"Emergencies, huh? That's a new one. And wait a second, you don't have your own computer."

"But I'm getting one. Dad promised me my own computer for my birthday."

"Oh he did? How old are you going to be on this most privileged of birthdays?"

"Fifteen."

"Fifteen? You know what kind of computer I had when I was fifteen?"

"Of course they didn't have computers when you were a teenager Mom. I don't think they even had radios or TVs."

"Yes, you're absolutely right. That's why I draw so well. All I had as a child was a broken pencil and a piece of paper. The room I shared with my sister didn't even need one electrical outlet because we didn't have electricity in those days either."

"Oh funny Mom."

"Anyway, it's not really the job of the architect to place the electrical outlets. When we hire an electrician, I'll let you talk to him about your five electrical outlets."

"Hire a cute electrician Mom."

"I'll hire an ugly, married electrician, Renata."

"You should have been a comedienne Mom."

Renata tossed her long, straight black hair over her shoulder and gave a sarcastic wave good-bye to her mother as she disappeared down the hallway. She entered Paloma's bedroom where she found her sister and her ponies scattered all over the floor.

"Pretty soon you and your ponies will have a new bedroom to play in Paloma. That'll be nice, won't it?"

"I guess so."

"Aren't you excited about the new house?"

"Not really. I like this house."

"But the new house is going to be bigger and prettier."

"I like it here. And besides, you'll be going to college soon so you won't even live there very long so why should you be so excited?"

"College is a long ways away Paloma."

"No it's not. It's only three years away and three years is not a long time."

"Well, I'm excited about moving to the new house and I think you should be too."

"Renata, what ocean is on the East Coast of the United States?"

"Atlantic, why?"

"It's geography homework. Here, look at this map. That's the only thing I couldn't remember. The rest is right, isn't it?"

"Canada has only one "n" but everything else is right. I didn't know you studied geography in third grade."

"When did you have geography?"

"I don't remember, but it wasn't third grade. Are you learning handwriting too?"

"We learned that a long time ago. I knew how to do handwriting in first grade."

"Gosh, I think they teach everything earlier now. You're growing up too fast Paloma."

"Yea, but you'll always be much older than me no matter how fast I grow up."

"Does that bother you?"

"Sometimes, like when you tell me not to mess with your things."

"Did you draw that flower?" Renata asked as she picked up a piece of paper from Paloma's notebook.

"Don't mess with my things," Paloma responded with a smile. "Yes, I drew it."

Paloma organized her papers and placed them in the desk, with the exception of one paper, which she folded and placed in her pocket.

Orpet joined Elida in the office as she continued working while sipping a cup of hot herbal tea. Outside the heavens had opened up and dumped a steady amount of rain on an already cool and gray afternoon. Orpet sat at his desk and logged on to his computer.

"Would you like some tea?" Elida asked as she set her pencil down for a moment.

"No thank you. Did we get the mail yet?" he asked.

"It's in the kitchen, just bills and junk mail. Your mother called this morning while you were out."

"Oh yea, what's up?"

"I don't know, something about houses and taxes."

"I already paid our tax bill for the house," Orpet shot back in disgust. "Since when do I need to be reminded about paying bills?"

"It's not for our house. Calm down; I'm not the one that called. It's something about your mother's house but I didn't pay much attention."

"Oh that's nice Elida. My mother calls and you can't even pay attention or take a message."

"Crucify me why don't you Orpet. Just pick up the phone and call her back."

"That's not the point."

"Why does there have to be a point?"

The rain pounded against the window even harder as Elida took another sip of tea and returned to her blueprint. Paloma entered the office and stood near her mother.

"How's the house coming?"

"Fine. Do you want to see where your bedroom will be?"

"Sure," Paloma said as she got closer to the easel.

"It's here at the end of the hall." Elida turned her pencil around and with the eraser end of it she pointed out different areas of the house. "Upstairs there will be four bedrooms. Yours will be at the end of the hall. The one on this side is Renata's and this one is Tiago's."

"Where's the window Mom? I want a window in my room, to look out and see the sky."

"We can install a window, Paloma," Elida answered with a smile. "We'll put a window in your room to see the sky."

The phone rang and Orpet answered it, on the first ring. He motioned to Elida and Paloma to quiet down so he could hear. Elida quietly suggested to Paloma to run along to her room. As she did, she removed the folded piece of paper from her pocket and placed it on Elida's bookcase.

"Sure, that'll be fine," Orpet answered into the phone as Elida looked at him curiously.

"We'll talk about it more tomorrow at the office...fine... bye."

"What was that about?" Elida asked as Orpet set the phone down.

"A conference, this Thursday and Friday."

"Where?" Elida asked, "Rio?"

"Not exactly," Orpet replied quickly. "Utah."

"What?" Elida threw her pencil down and stood up. "Come on Orpet, we had plans this weekend, and we've got to get out to the construction site this week."

"I'll be home Saturday afternoon so it won't ruin your weekend plans and we can see the site early next week."

"Fine, we'll do everything around your schedule, like always."

"Enough Elida, come on."

"Come on nothing," she responded as she walked away and instinctively picked up the piece of paper that Paloma had left on the bookcase. "You've been traveling too much and I don't like it."

Orpet didn't respond and Elida walked out of the office. She entered the kitchen and put some more water in the kettle to boil for tea. Just as soon as she turned on the burner and placed the kettle on it, she turned the burner off, put some water in her mug and placed it in the microwave. As she waited, she unfolded the piece of paper that Paloma had written and began to read. Renata came into the kitchen and for some reason that she herself wasn't sure of, Elida stopped reading and put the note in her pocket as if she were hiding something.

"You and Dad fighting?" Renata asked rather nonchalantly.

"Not really," Elida responded as she took the mug out of the microwave. "He's just traveling again and I don't like it."

Elida took her tea and Paloma's note into the living room where she sat down and continued reading.

"Mommy I love you"
"I'll never be apart from you"
"signed: Paloma"

Elida sat back on the couch and gazed outside at the teeming rain. A cold chill came over her so she grasped the mug with both hands to feel the warmth on her hands. She looked at Paloma's note again and suddenly felt very warm and happy. Paloma just did that for her, she thought to herself. She sat on the couch awhile as she finished her tea. Afterwards she walked back towards the office. The door to Paloma's room was shut so Elida continued to the office.

"Elida, listen," Orpet said immediately as he stood up from his desk.

"Don't worry about it honey," she said just as quickly. "I know you have to travel. It'll be fine, as long as you're home on Saturday."

"I will be, early afternoon for sure. Lord knows I don't want to spend a Saturday night in Utah."

"Could be fun, who knows?" she said with a smile as she sat back down at her easel.

Orpet walked over to the easel and from behind he kissed Elida on the top of her head.

"Kiss her good Dad," Renata yelled out as she walked by in the hallway. "Kiss her good or she'll draw a bedroom on that blueprint for you outside with Wolf."

Chapter 8

The school bus carrying Mrs. Allagoas' third grade class rumbled around the curve that stretched to the peak of the mountainous state park and brought its huge tires to a stop in the gravel that marked a clearance in the heavily wooded area.

The six parents who volunteered to don their oldest pair of jeans and their dirtiest walking shoes to help supervise the field trip hopped down from the bus ahead of the children. They lined up as a guard unit in an attempt to restore the discipline that had temporarily been lost during the 45-minute drive.

The typically juvenile yet harmless antics like bouncing up and down on the seats, shouting across the aisles and singing disparaging songs about fellow classmates had left the bus driver a bit anxious, but Mrs. Allagoas and the six parents, by virtue of a more patient and understanding demeanor, managed to suppress any potential uprising.

Paloma jumped down the steps of the bus with the other children. She was dressed in the best camouflage outfit that Elida could put together.

"I have to wear something that won't scare the animals," Paloma instructed her mother as she got ready in the morning. "I need Army clothes, something like that."

Elida was able to find only an old tie-dye shirt streaked with bold pink and red lines, a faded pair of blue jeans and a straw hat. Paloma stood in front of the mirror in her bedroom and with her hands on her hips she shook her head in disapproval. "The way I am, all the animals will immediately know that I am a person."

Three park rangers, properly and professionally attired in durable cotton one-piece outfits, canvas hiking boots and backpacks, greeted the group and instructed them to form a circle for a brief orientation.

"Good morning and welcome to the forest," shouted a short and robust young woman who looked like she had just stepped off the set of Crocodile Dundee. "My name is Rachel and I want to welcome you all to this very special place. Today you are going on an adventure that I'm sure you'll enjoy. The land that you'll hike over is the same land on which early Indians once lived and you'll learn, as you hike, a lot about how those Indians lived. Before we get started I want to introduce you to the two tall gentlemen standing underneath that eucalyptus tree. They will be joining me in helping you throughout your hike and I believe they have some important words to say before we leave."

A man, probably in his fifties, with a long dark beard and a stout body that appeared more like that of a thirty year old, stepped forward and into the center of the circle and introduced himself as Joe.

"Good morning boys and girls. What I'd like to tell you before we begin our hike is that in order to have fun today, there is one very important thing that all of you must remember. You will see many plants and flowers today and you will learn how the Indians who once lived here used these items in their lives, including which of them they were able to use as food. However, since this land is wild and since you do not yet have the knowledge that the Indians had, it's very important that you avoid touching and especially tasting anything unless one of the guides gives you the approval to do so. Some of the plants you'll see are poisonous and we certainly don't want anyone to get sick today."

"Very good reminder," Rachel said as Joe backed up against the tree and tightened his backpack around his shoulders. "I now want you to pay close attention to Paulo who also has some important words for you."

"I would like to talk a little bit about some friends we'll be visiting today," said Paulo, a muscular, rugged young man with dirty blonde hair and blue eyes. "Hopefully today you will get a chance to see some of the animals that live in this area. There are many different kinds of birds here, there are many land animals like armadillos and anteaters and there are also a variety of snakes and lizards. What I want you to remember as you see these animals is that this land is their home and you are a visitor in their house. Just like you would not want a visitor in your house to scream at you, or wake you up if you were sleeping, or pick you up and carry you across the house or disturb the things in your room, I don't want to see anyone disturbing the house of our little friends. If we treat them nicely, they'll be happy and they'll let you get a good look at them. If you are not nice; however, they'll become upset and scared and they'll run away and we won't be able to enjoy them."

"Are there any poisonous snakes?" a young boy called out with a hint of fear in his voice.

"Yes there are," Paulo replied, "and that's why it's extremely important that we stay together, listen to the guides and keep our hands to ourselves."

Rachel walked to the center of the circle as Paulo stepped back and joined Joe under the eucalyptus tree. She thanked her two assistants for their contribution to the orientation and then began organizing the group for the hike. She divided the six parents into pairs and lined them up in front of three rows of children, ten in each row. She assigned a guide to each group and then appointed Mrs. Allagoas as the honorary guide for the whole group.

It was a cool and crisp morning but by 10:00, nearly one hour into the hike, the sun began finding its way through the trees and the children began removing their sweaters and sweat shirts and strategically tying them around their waists like professional hikers.

They had cautiously steered away from the patches of poison oak and gleefully tasted the samples of mint leaves and butter lettuce. They had peeled away strands from the yucca plants which the Indians had used to make, among other things, their huts and they had gathered a light collection of "makeup rocks" as Rachel called them, grainy reddish rocks that when rubbed against the face served as a primitive form of rouge. The boys rubbed the rocks against their arms and created their own tattoos.

By noon the three groups had convened by the river that had become the point of excitement and anticipation. Crossing the slowly rushing river in shoes and socks and regular clothes was the type of adventure that the third graders were looking forward to.

Along the banks of the river, as the children waited for their turn to cross, Paulo pointed out in the hardened soil, the footprints of a small animal. Upon the request of a curious young animal lover, Paulo pulled out his pocket knife and began to carve the block of soil. He managed to lift the piece up in its entirety but as he transferred it to the boy, the soil crumbled and the footprint, which they determined probably belonged to a badger, disappeared.

"You shouldn't have messed with their house," another boy commented to Paulo who laughed as he accepted the legitimate criticism.

The group trudged their wet bodies, many of which had fallen into the river, to a clearing on the north side where several picnic tables sat waiting to accommodate the hungry hikers. While the children ate their lunches and visited the portable toilets that the Indians did not have the privilege of using, Paulo set up his rope-making demonstration which would kick off the second half of the journey.

As the children formed a circle at Paulo's feet, Mrs.

Allagoas noticed Paloma sitting alone under a tree.

"Don't you want to come see how the Indians used to make rope?" Mrs. Allagoas asked as she sat down on the grass next to Paloma.

"Yes, I'll be right there."

"Is there something wrong Paloma?"

"No, why?"

"I don't know, I just found it strange that you are sitting here all alone."

"I'm just relaxing and enjoying nature."

"That's good. Are you having a good time?"

"Oh yes. I really love it here. Nature is so beautiful."

"I think so too. Come, let's go watch the rope demonstration."

"I'll be right there Mrs. Allagoas. I want to sit for a little longer."

Paulo took a handful of the long strands of grass that he collected and began weaving them into a rope. "Twist and wrap is the technique that we use," Paulo explained as he carefully manipulated the thick grass. "We twist this bunch very tightly in one direction and then wrap it over the next bunch in the opposite direction to form a strong bond."

Within minutes Paulo had woven a rope of about five feet and then to test its strength he held one end and conducted a tug-of-war contest with a group of children who held the other end. The winner was clearly the rope itself as it stayed strong and firm despite the tugging.

Paulo gave the rope to Mrs. Allagoas as a gift which she proudly held throughout the remainder of the hike. She hung it above her desk in the classroom and the next day pointed towards it as an idea for the children to help them with their assignment.

"What I want you to do," Mrs. Allagoas said to the class, "is to write a one-page essay about what you liked most about your field trip to the forest. This rope could be one idea. You could write about the demonstration that Paulo gave and how the Indians may have used the rope. Or you could write about crossing the river, or a special plant you saw or an animal you saw. It's up to you. Just make your essays interesting and make sure that your spelling and your grammar are good."

The class was silent as each student began writing but soon the recollections of the day before caused them to make little comments which spurned further discussions and laughter.

"Quiet!" Mrs. Allagoas insisted as she sat at her desk, under her rope.

Paloma sat at her desk which was to the right of Mrs. Allagoas' desk. She did not get caught up in the conversation of her peers; instead she diligently worked until the morning bell and then proudly turned in her paper.

Just as soon as all fifteen children were seated and reasonably quiet, Tomas Castro, the school district's oldest and most experienced driver, gave a tug on the lever that closed the narrow double doors and the golden mini-bus pulled slowly away from the curb. Paloma sat alone on the front steps of the elementary school, pleasantly pleased that the bus was leaving without her.

Giving in, as she so often did to Paloma's insistence not to ride the bus, Elida had agreed to pick her up at the school after aerobics.

"I just don't like it," was all that Paloma would say when Elida questioned her dislike for riding the bus.

Paloma hopped down the steps as she saw the brown station wagon turn into the school parking lot but to her surprise, Elida parked the car instead of driving up to the curb. Paloma waited with a perplexed look on her face as her mother walked towards the school.

"What are you doing Mommy? Why did you park the car?"

"I have to go in to speak with your teacher. She called me at home and said she wanted to see me."

"What did I do?"

"I don't know. I was going to ask you that."

"I didn't do anything Mom."

"So there's nothing to worry about."

Elida led Paloma through the front door and down the hallway past the auditorium where the second-graders were rehearsing their play.

"Why don't you get a book to read," she said to Paloma as they stopped in front of the library. "I won't be long."

Elida watched a moment as Paloma sat herself down at an empty table. Instead of going for a book, Paloma pulled a pencil out of her backpack and began writing in her notebook. She lifted her eyes from the page and somewhat inadvertently met Elida's eyes in a puzzling way. She returned her attention to the notebook as Elida turned and walked away.

Elida knocked softly on the closed door of Mrs. Allagoas' third grade classroom. She peered through the small window on the door and saw the teacher peering back as she walked towards the door.

"Hello, come on in," Mrs. Allagoas said with a warm smile as she led Elida into the busy and cluttered work environment that she had been calling home for nearly twenty years. "Please excuse the mess," she apologized to Elida, "today was hectic and I haven't yet had time to organize a thing."

"No need to apologize, believe me, I know you have your hands full."

"Well, we manage. It's all part of the job description."

Mrs. Allagoas led Elida to her desk where she set aside her own chair for her guest to sit.

"Please, sit here," she said politely. "I'm sorry I bothered you at home today. I hope I didn't disrupt anything."

"No, not at all," Elida replied.

"I have been wanting to talk with you for quite some time," the teacher began, leaning uncomfortably against her desk. "In the beginning of the year I wanted to talk with you because I was having some difficulties with Paloma. She has a very strong personality and I hadn't quite found the proper way to relate to her. There were some incidents with other children that seemed to make Paloma very reclusive and I wasn't sure what to make of it. But I watched her closely and I managed to talk to her on several occasions and I began to understand her reclusive personality and her solitude. She is very different from the others, in fact, more different than any child I've seen. She is actually extraordinary, and I say that mainly with regards to her abilities in communication and expression. While at times she is reclusive, she is also deeply profound in the way she opens up and expresses herself. I say these things with the highest regard you understand."

"She seems to enjoy school and she speaks of you fondly," Elida replied after a short, awkward silence as she absorbed Mrs. Allagoas' compliments. "I think she's doing well."

"I do too; that's why I called you in today."

"I'm not sure I understand."

"You know that we went on a field trip yesterday."

"Of course, to the forest. Paloma told me all about it. She was very excited."

"I know she was. Well this morning I had the children write essays about what they enjoyed most about the trip. I read most of them today during lunch."

"And you read Paloma's?"

"More than once. Her essay was amazing. Most of the children wrote about the games they played on the bus or the fun they had crossing the river or playing tug-of-war with the rope we made. Their essays were nice but they were simplistic. Paloma wrote about nature. She wrote about how beautiful the sky was, how warm the sun was, how green the grass was. It was a lovely essay, really lovely. I'll show it to you."

"She told me last night how much she loved the trip and how beautiful it was."

"She also wrote, I remember," Mrs. Allagoas continued as she leafed through the folder of essays looking for Paloma's, "a few lines about the animals and she said something like, 'How lovely to lead the life of an animal; prancing about through a carefree day.' It was so beautiful and so unusual for a child of her age."

"Paloma loves to write and she writes well. Often times she'll write me little notes and poems that I would agree are unusual for a young girl. It's kind of weird actually."

"The minds of the world's greatest poets have often been described as weird. Paloma is a poet, an artist. The fact that we may not be able to fully comprehend what's in her mind does not make her weird. Anyway, I didn't mean to bother you today. I just wanted to bring this to your attention because I think it's an extraordinary thing and something you should be very proud of."

"I am very proud of Paloma and I appreciate all you've done for her."

Elida held Paloma's hand for the entire drive home from school. She was unusually happy and she carried that feeling around the kitchen as she prepared dinner with Renata.

"What did Paloma's teacher want to see you about?" Renata asked.

"She just wanted to show me an essay she wrote. Renata, slice the potatoes in quarters. They're easier to mash when they're in smaller pieces.

"What was the essay about?"

"It was about the field trip she went on."

"What was wrong with the essay?"

"Wash off the potatoes and put the water to boil. Actually, nothing was wrong with the essay. Mrs. Allagoas wanted me to see it because it was so good."

"Paloma's a good writer. Maybe she'll write a book when she grows up."

"Mom...!" Paloma called out from the backyard. "Come here Mom."

"Not right now Paloma, I'm making dinner. Renata, did

you finish making the salad dressing?"

"It's in the refrigerator. I think it's good."

"Mom! Come outside and see the sunset! Run Mom!"

"But Paloma, I have to finish in the kitchen."

"Come Mom!" Paloma insisted.

"Renata, keep an eye on the potatoes. Just turn the heat down when they become soft."

"Mom, come look at the sky!" Paloma said cheerfully as her mother walked into the backyard. "Look at the sunset Mom. Isn't it the prettiest?"

"Yes, it really is. It's such a bright orange. I haven't seen it that bright in a long time."

"And the lines of red too Mom. It's beautiful!"

Elida took Paloma's hand and the two walked together along the rough of the fairway of the third hole. The big orange beach ball slowly descended on the horizon but its glow left a vivid illumination upon the golf course. The plush and evenly cut grass gently cushioned their feet as they casually walked. The air was fresh and filled with the distinctive scent from a row of trees that lined the fairway.

"If the sun and the sky is this beautiful Mom, just imagine how beautiful heaven must be. Don't you think heaven must be beautiful?"

Elida paused and stared at Paloma as she weighed the heavy question.

"Yes, it must be beautiful," she finally said. "And how about trees," she continued in a more lively tone of voice. "I think trees are so amazing. Stop and think how amazing it is that they can grow so tall and live for so long."

"Would you want to live as long as a tree does Mom?"

Elida did not have time to ponder or answer Paloma's question. From the row of trees near to where they walked came a sudden, loud crashing noise that stunned both Paloma and Elida. They looked at each other in fright and then looked towards the trees. Paloma screamed and ran all at the same time, leaving Elida behind for just a moment.

At the base of the tree, in the tall grass that made up the farthest edge of the boundaries of the golf course, was a fairly large, black and blue bird. It lay in the grass absolutely motionless. Paloma knelt in the grass within a careful distance of the bird and looked intently at it. Elida grabbed Paloma from the back and pulled her away a bit.

"Is it dead Mom?"

"I don't know."

Elida inched closer to the subject and looked carefully at it. She tried to detect a heartbeat or any movement whatsoever but there was none. It was obvious that the bird was dead.

"Why don't we pray," Elida suggested to Paloma.

Just as she said that, Elida tried to take the words back. How absurd, she thought to herself. She had wanted to pray with Paloma before and she had refused. Now, outside in the grass with a lost, dead bird at their side, Elida had suggested praying. To her surprise, however, Paloma reached out and held the bird and agreed to pray. Elida extended her hand towards Paloma's and they quietly prayed. Moments into their prayer, Elida stopped and again thought to herself how ludicrous, and even how wrong, it was to have Paloma praying over a dead bird. She listened and watched as Paloma continued and then she silently disregarded her awkward feelings and prayed together once more.

In the very instance that they finished their prayer together, not a second before and not a second after, the bird twitched its wings inside Paloma's palm and jerked its body free of her grasp. In a sweeping, sudden yet beautifully fluid motion, the bird took flight and disappeared above the trees.

Elida screeched in shock and disbelief. Paloma, much to the contrary, sat calmly in the grass and looked upwards with a satisfying and peaceful look on her face. Somehow, not only had Paloma's prayer been answered, but Paloma had known that it would.

"Mom...! Mom, come here...!" The sounds of Tiago's shrill voice traveled quickly in the evening air and Elida and Paloma were startled as they saw him running down the fairway. "Come back Mom, Renata needs you in the kitchen."

Elida suddenly realized that her extended and quite unusual nature walk with Paloma had taken her mind miles away from the dinner on the stove and in the oven. By the time she made her way back to the house, she realized just how far away her mind had drifted.

"Renata! What happened?"

"What happened Mom? What happened is that you told me to watch the potatoes which I did but you said nothing about the roast beef in the oven which is now burnt."

"Oh shoot!" Elida hollered at herself as she opened the door on the oven which had a dark smoke seeping from its edges. "It's more than burnt."

"You didn't tell me to take it out Mom. I didn't think of it until I saw the smoke."

"It's my fault Renata."

"Where were you Mom?"

Elida looked glumly at Renata and then turned towards Paloma who stood silently in the doorway to the back yard. She then turned back to Renata. "I was praying dear, praying."

Chapter 9

"Switzerland."

Paloma slowly and precisely pronounced the word over and over again as she looked through the pages of her Children's World Atlas.

"Europe, it's in Europe Paloma; you're looking at Asia," Tiago said helpfully as he sat next to his sister on the living room couch.

Orpet broke the news gently to the family, and especially to Elida, about his upcoming trip to Switzerland for a series of conferences. He would be gone for two weeks which is about as long as any trip he'd taken. But this was also among the most important trips he had taken for the Navy and he was very excited about the opportunity. Elida wasn't as excited.

"Do you know the names of any major cities in Switzerland?" Orpet quizzed Renata who sat on the floor of the living room, leafing through a magazine.

"Tokyo Dad. Mom, what are we having for dinner?"

"Zurich," Tiago blurted out.

"Spaghetti," Elida told Renata.

"Geneva too," Tiago added.

"That's where I'll be," Orpet said. "All of the conferences will be in Geneva."

"When are you leaving Dad?" Paloma asked.

"Next week. I leave on Monday."

"We should eat," Elida said, unamused by the talk of another business trip. Over dinner, Elida steered the conversation away from Switzerland to the construction of the new house. They ate hurriedly as Orpet had arranged a meeting with the contractor and he promised to take everyone with him as long as there were no delays.

"When do you think we'll move in?" Tiago asked his father as he twirled his spaghetti around his plate with a fork.

"Hey, use the spoon Tiago," Renata interrupted, "you're gonna wind up twirling that spaghetti on the floor any minute."

"I'll twirl it onto your lap in a minute."

"Get a life."

"Just eat," Orpet said, putting an end to the conversation that was creating the delay he knew would come.

"So when are we moving Dad?"

"Not for a while Tiago. Just eat."

"There's a long way to go still," Elida said more calmly. "Even when the house looks ready, the finishings and small details take a long time. We won't be moving until after the winter, if all goes well."

"Do they eat spaghetti in Switzerland Dad?" Paloma asked after a short silence.

"We're leaving in five minutes," Orpet said as he got up from the table and took his dish to the sink. "I don't know Paloma, I'm sure they eat spaghetti in Switzerland. Five minutes," he said again as he walked towards the office, "And bring sweaters, it'll be colder later."

"Mom, are we staying at the house until after it's dark?" Paloma asked as she finished eating.

"Probably not, you can't see anything there when it's dark."

"Good. I don't want to change and I don't want to wear a sweater."

"Paloma, you heard your father. It'll be colder later. You will change your skirt. Put on some long pants and put on your pink sweater."

"No."

Paloma got up from the table, cleared her plate and walked

to her room. Orpet passed her in the hallway on his way back to the kitchen.

"Put on the pants Paloma," he said.

"No."

"Put on the pants or stay home."

"No."

"Sweetie, do what your father said," Elida pleaded as she followed Paloma into her room. Paloma sat at her desk and tapped her fingers. "It's going to be cold and you shouldn't be out there with bare legs."

"Mom, Dad doesn't know anything about dressing girls."

"We're leaving," Orpet shouted from the kitchen as he organized some papers needed for the contractor. Renata and Tiago waited in the hallway, with sweaters.

"Paloma, they're leaving," Elida continued. "Put on the pants."

"I don't like long pants Mom. I like this skirt."

"We're leaving," Orpet said as he passed by the bedroom. "Are you putting on a pair of pants and coming or are you staying?"

"I told you, I'm wearing this skirt and I'm going."

Paloma folded her arms across her chest, dug her chin down towards the floor and began walking out of the bedroom. Before she could get one foot into the hallway, however, Orpet reached out his right arm, grabbed Paloma by the pony tail and dragged her back into the room. A cold, piercing shriek echoed throughout the house.

"Don't you start your crying Paloma," Orpet said firmly.

"Stop Dad!"

"No Paloma, I can't allow you to behave like this," he said, now yelling.

"I'm not doing anything."

"And you're not going out either."

"Good! I don't want to go to the stupid house anyway. I don't ever want to live there."

"Stop it Paloma, just stop this behavior now."

Orpet led Elida out of the bedroom and slammed the door behind him.

"Well, that's just great."

"Orpet, I'll stay here. You go. I can talk to her again later."

"We're leaving. Renata and Tiago let's go. You can talk to her all you want. We'll be back in a couple of hours."

"Paloma's not going Dad?" Tiago asked as his father hurried out of the front door.

"No, she's not. Let's go."

Elida watched the car pull out of the driveway. She wiped her eyes and let out a deep agonizing breath. As she walked down the hallway, she heard Paloma's continuous screeching bouncing off the walls. She paused briefly in front of Paloma's room but decided not to enter.

Elida sat at her easel, slowly stroking the lines that formed an old cobblestone road. On the left side of the road stood a row of dingy, decrepit single-story houses and on the right side stood a magnificently brilliant white church with a tall steeple that reached towards a crystal blue sky. Seated on the curb in front of one of the houses was a young boy. His clothing was tattered, his hair was disheveled and his eyes were filled with bewilderment as he gazed upwards at the steeple.

Elida's brush froze in the middle of the cobblestone road as she suddenly realized that the house was now quiet. She placed the brush down and walked slowly out of the office. She knocked gently on the bedroom door but got no response.

"Paloma? May I come in?"

"I'm busy Mom."

"Busy doing what?"

"I'm writing."

"Would you like some tea? I'm going to make some for myself. I'll make a cup for you if you'd like."

"No Mom. No tea."

"O.K. I'll be in the office if you need anything."

Elida returned to her easel but decided not to continue painting. Just then, the phone rang. It was Heloisa, Orpet's cousin. Elida wanted to speak about Paloma, hoping her cousin would give her some encouraging words on how to deal with Paloma's recent bout with temper and anxiety. Instead, for some reason that she couldn't figure out, she refrained completely from mentioning anything at all. "The kids are fine," was all that she managed to say.

They talked about the new house and how pleased Elida was with how the design turned out. They talked about Orpet's upcoming trip to Europe and how excited he was about that. They talked about Elida's mother, who was presently visiting a friend in Santos. They talked about money, which they both concluded there was never enough of, and they talked a little about sex, which they reached the same conclusion about.

Suddenly, Elida heard a scratching noise coming from the doorway. She watched in disbelief as two white pieces of paper slid slowly under the door. She then heard faint footsteps atop the fluffy carpet as Paloma returned to her room.

Elida walked over to the door, dragging the telephone with her, and picked up the papers. She tucked them inside her pocket without mentioning anything to her cousin about what had happened. The curiosity and concern did force her, however, to cut short the conversation and hang up.

With the notes still in her pocket, Elida walked slowly out of the office and down the hallway to the bedroom once again. She didn't enter, instead she continued into the kitchen. She held the notes in her hand as she turned on the stove to boil water for tea. As she stood waiting for the water to boil, she unfolded the notes and began to read.

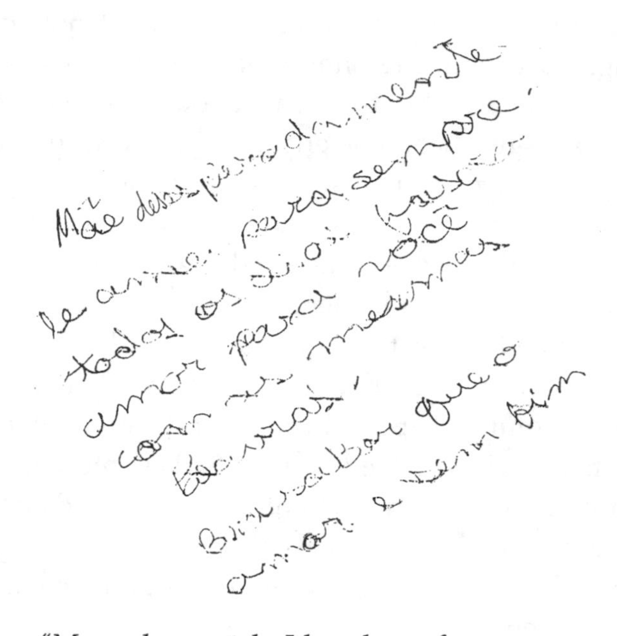
Mãe desesperadamente
te amei para sempre.
todos os dias faço
amor para você
com as mesmas
palavras
Para saber que o
amor é sem fim

"Mom, desperately I loved you forever...
Every day I make love for you with the same words
so that you will know that love is endless"

Quando você morrer
já mais esquecerei de
você.
Você me dá o carinho
e o amor e o meu troco
é o amor mais lindo do mundo

"When you die I'll never forget you.
You give me tenderness and love and my exchange
is the most beautiful love in the world"

mamãe você acha que
eu sou uma bebê de 1 ano
Pode ficar achando
Por ninguém gosta de
mim
E se eu não sou amada
por ninguém pra que
eu fui excistir

"Mommy you think that I am a one year old baby.
You can keep thinking that. But nobody loves me.
And if I'm not loved by anyone for what did I exist." [sic.]

me tranquei eu quero
morrer
pode gosar da minha
cara.
pois eu vou morrer
a qualquer dia da in-
fansia

"I locked myself in I want to die.
You can make fun of me but I'm going to die any day in my infancy."

A deafening, shrill whistle rang out inside Elida's head and jolted her. She shook nervously and then noticed that the water in the kettle was now boiling.

Chapter 10

"But Doctor, if this is not something to worry about, what is?"

"Wait, wait, wait. Let's first use the proper vocabulary. I don't believe the word worry belongs in the dictionary. Worrying is among man's least productive activities. To worry is to fail to make a legitimate attempt to solve a problem. If it's beyond your control or absolutely impossible to solve a given problem, then put your mind's energy to a better use. If the problem can be solved, then just do it."

"You make it sound so easy." Elida said to Dr. Wagner, a family counselor.

"Quite on the contrary. Taking action, rather than sitting around and worrying, is a difficult task. But nothing worth having or doing comes easy. It takes a struggle. Let's struggle through this one."

"I'm scared Doctor."

"Of course you're scared. You love your daughter and your daughter is experiencing pain right now. You feel her pain. That's good."

"I don't feel very good. When I read her note I was in shock. I felt an immense pain all throughout my body. I just worry for her, whether that's the right thing to do or not I don't know, but it's what I do."

"What exactly do you worry about?"

"I worry about her temper and I want to teach her to control it for her own good. I know and I see the sweetness behind her temper but others won't see it and that will hurt her in her future. It's my function as a mother to help her."

"This isn't the first time she's written notes to you, right?"

"She writes and draws for me often, beautiful messages, but lately the subject matter and the style have intensified."

"Has she made references to death before?"

"Yes. A short while ago she mentioned in a note how she would never forget me when I died."

"That's natural."

"Natural? Natural for an average 8-year-old girl to be talking about death. Come on."

"This is not an average 8-year-old girl. This is a girl with an extraordinarily deep emotional capacity. This is a girl full of love and passion for her mother. Listen to her words with your heart, not just with your ears. Read those notes over again with your heart, not just with your eyes. She's reaching out to you. Embrace her, love her back and you'll help her."

"I can do that, but that might be only half of the solution."

"What's the other half?"

"Her father. I haven't even told him about this. He's away on business. I'm afraid he'll punish her and punishment will make her only worse."

"You'll have to decide what role your husband will play, but clearly, hiding something as significant as this is not the way to go."

"I know that. Of course I intend on telling him everything. But he's very stern with the children and I don't think stern is what's needed right now."

"I'll tell you exactly what's needed right now and needed all the time. This will be the most important lesson on parenting you'll ever receive and since it's not my own advice, I'll turn the clock off and give it to you free. Have you read this book?"

"*The Prophet*, by Kahlil Gibran? Yes, I have it at home."

"I'm sure you do. Many people do. But have you read it? Have you read it the way I've asked you to read your daughter's notes?"

"I suppose I haven't."

"Open the book to page 17. Read the passage. Read it aloud, slowly, reading with your heart, not just with your eyes and your voice."

Your children are not your children.
They are the sons and daughters of Life's longing for itself.
They come through you but not from you,
And though they are with you they belong not to you.
You may give them your love but not your thoughts,
For they have their own thoughts.
You may house their bodies but not their souls,
For their souls dwell in the house of tomorrow, which you cannot visit, not even in your dreams.
You may strive to be like them, but seek not to make them like you.
For life goes not backward nor tarries with yesterday.
You are the bow from which your children as living arrows are sent forth.
The archer sees the mark upon the path of the infinite, and He bends you with His might that His arrow may go swift and far.
Let your bending in the archer's hand be for gladness;
For even as He loves the arrow that flies, so He loves also the bow that is stable."

Elida fingered through the row of books along the top shelf of the bookcase in the office and found *The Prophet* stuck between *The Road Less Traveled* and *Your Sacred Self.* As she pulled the book from the shelf, she reflected with regret on how little time she had for simple pleasures like reading. And now she was reading not to gain pleasure, but to relieve pain.

She walked to the bedroom, sat at the edge of the bed and opened the book to page 17. She read the passage over and over again.

> *"Your children are not your children...*
> *...they belong not to you.*
> *You may house their bodies but not their souls...*
> *...life goes not backward..."*

How could she possibly let go of Paloma? How could she accept the idea that Paloma was not really hers? Paloma was as much a part of her as her own arms and legs.

She closed the book and fell onto the bed. The day was calm, the house was silent. The bow was stable.

There was a knock at the bedroom door and Renata gently poked her head inside. "I'm sorry to bother you Mom, but we decided to set the table and make lunch for you and Paloma's not helping. Can you please tell her to help?"

"Don't get excited Renata. Where is she?"

"She's just sitting out front."

"Come here Renata. I want to talk to you. Close the door."

"What is it Mom?"

"Renata, Paloma is not herself lately. She's a bit troubled. I'm not exactly sure what it is or what's wrong, but it's something that we need to pay attention to. I need both Tiago and you to make an extra special effort to be patient with her."

"Mom, we always need to be patient with Paloma. She's always a bit troubled."

"Renata, please. I need your help. Just be nice, that's all."

"Fine Mom. Come for lunch in ten minutes. We'll have it ready."

After lunch, Renata and Tiago willingly cleared the table and did the dishes. Elida changed her clothes and put on some makeup to freshen her sullen and tired face. Paloma sat quietly on the floor in her bedroom, slowly combing the mane of her aqua blue pony.

"Would you like to go to the mall with me?" Elida asked Paloma as she entered her bedroom.

"Just you and me?"

"Yes, just you and me."

Elida took Paloma by the hand and led her down the hallway. They picked up their coats in the closet and stopped off in the kitchen to say good-bye to Renata and Tiago. Elida took a back road to the mall to avoid the monotony of the freeway. A slight rain began spattering on the windshield, but nothing severe enough to obstruct the pretty view of the fields and the trees that passed by. Paloma spotted a group of cows huddled under an oak tree not far from the road and reminded Elida that they needed to stop at the market on the way home to buy milk.

The rain fell at a steady clip as Elida turned into the parking lot of the shopping mall. Having left their umbrellas where they usually did when it rained - at home - the two stared at each other as they contemplated the distance between the car and the entrance to the mall.

"At least you know how to swim," Elida joked with Paloma.

"Backstroke on cement? I don't think so."

"I know what we'll do. We'll drive over to the entrance, I'll drop you off and then I'll park the car and walk back to you. That way only one of us gets wet."

"No Mom. I want to stay with you. If you get wet, I get wet."

"O.K. I'll drop you off, you go into the store and buy an umbrella, walk back to the car with the umbrella and then we walk back together. That way nobody gets wet."

"And we get into the mall at midnight. That's a silly idea."

"Well, what's your idea?"

"I say we just run for it."

"But it's raining so hard. I don't want to get soaked."

"We have to do a lot of things in life that we don't want to Mom."

"Oh great. I'm stuck in the rain with a philosopher."

Elida climbed over to the passenger seat, held Paloma by the hand and slowly opened the door. Immediately a splash of water landed rudely in their laps, forcing Elida to slam the door shut.

"Let's go home Paloma."

"Don't be a chicken Mom. Let's go for it."

Racing in front, Paloma led Elida by the hand across the parking lot. They giggled wildly as the rain drenched their faces and tickled their feet. Elida gave a huge sigh of relief as they reached the overhang at the mall entrance. She shook herself like a dog just out of a bath tub.

"See Mom," Paloma said, "we did it!"

Elida took the cold, wet, chill from her body with a cappuccino at the small French cafe in the center of the mall. Paloma ordered a dish of chocolate ice cream which Elida did not quite understand considering the weather outside, but like other matters concerning Paloma that she didn't quite understand, Elida refrained from questioning too much.

"Would you like some chocolate sauce or some caramel sauce?"

"No Mom, this is fine. How's your coffee?"

"Delicious. Have you ever tried cappuccino?"

"No, what is it?"

"It's a strong coffee mixed with steamed milk. The way I like it, they sprinkle chocolate on the top."

"No thank you."

"You know, your birthday is only one month away so while we walk through the mall, take a look at some things you might want for your birthday."

"I just haven't thought about it Mom."

Elida dropped the subject right there, realizing that Paloma was not yet excited about her birthday. She tried hard to think of something that would animate Paloma, but visions of the note blocked her mind and her good intentions.

"Mom, how long is Grandma going to stay in our house," Paloma asked, breaking a short but awkward silence.

She was referring to Dora, who came when Orpet left on his trip.

"Actually, she'll be with us the whole time your father's in Switzerland and maybe a little while after that."

"Oh good. I like her. I really want her to stay. She's so much fun to be around."

"I'm so glad to hear you say that Paloma. I know she loves being around you."

Elida squirmed in her seat and looked down into the empty mug in front of her. Never before had she felt awkward and nervous and so very uncomfortable when talking to Paloma.

"I'm going to have another cappuccino. Would you like some more ice cream or maybe something to drink?"

"Just a glass of water Mom. Thanks."

"This coffee is really delicious," Elida said as she returned to the table. "It hits the spot."

"I miss you Mom. I miss you every day."

"What do you mean, you miss me? I'm right here sweetie."

"When you go away from me, like you just did. I miss you."

"Paloma, that's so sweet," Elida said as she ruffled her fingers through her daughter's hair. "I miss you too. I love you more than anything in this world. And I love having coffee and ice cream with you, just you and me."

Paloma gave a huge smile, the first such smile Elida had seen in days. The mall was busy around them, but for the moment, Elida felt comfortably all alone with Paloma. She felt good; the first such feeling she had experienced in days.

"Let's go shopping Paloma."

"When the going gets tough, the tough go shopping. Right Mom?"

"The going's not tough Paloma. Everything's going to be all right."

The rain had stopped when they left the mall just after 10:00 PM, so they had no difficulty walking to the car with their handful of bags. Aside from socks and underwear for Paloma; a blouse, a nightgown, some makeup and a blow dryer for herself; a flea collar for Wolf and a desk lamp for the office, Elida had found little to buy in the mall.

"Nothing for us?" Tiago asked as he and Renata sat on the couch watching TV when they arrived home.

"You know those sales. They never have anything special."

"I can see," Tiago laughed as he looked at the pile of bags on the living room table.

"Have you guys eaten?" Elida asked.

"Yes Mom. And we did the dishes too. You can relax."

"Thanks. That's just what I want to do. I'm going to take a hot shower."

"Would you like to watch TV with us?" Tiago asked Paloma as she stood alone at the table organizing the shopping bags.

"No thank you. I'm going to my room."

Paloma walked slowly down the hallway towards her room. She continued down the hallway and stopped outside of her parent's bedroom. She waited until the sound of her mother's shower was heard. Paloma entered the room quietly and sat on her mother's side of the bed, next to the night stand. She opened the top drawer of the night stand and saw a pile of papers, many of which she recognized from her own paper collection. She stared blankly at the contents of the drawer but did not touch anything.

By the time Elida got out of the shower, neither Paloma nor a trace of her entrance were in the room. Elida dressed in her new nightgown and walked towards the living room where the sound of the TV distracted her from the silence of the bedrooms.

"Where's Paloma?" she asked her two older children.

"In her room," Renata said with her face buried in a pillow. "Was she nervous in the mall Mom?"

"She was much better. Thank you both for being so understanding. I'm going to bed. Turn off the TV when you're finished please."

"Good night Mom," Renata and Tiago said simultaneously.

Elida knocked on the bedroom door but there was no answer. She entered to find Paloma sound asleep, still dressed and on top of the covers. The curtain was open; the light of the moon and the dim but majestic reflection of the eucalyptus trees blanketed the bed. Elida removed Paloma's shoes, tucked her under the covers and gently kissed her on the cheek.

"Sleep tight," she whispered in Paloma's ear, "sleep tight."

Chapter 11

Elida rose early the next day and brought a hot cup of coffee to the office where she eagerly sat down at her easel. The bright morning sunshine illuminated the white church and the cobblestone road of her painting, but the boy seated on the curb remained in a shadowy and foggy malaise.

She worked alone for close to two hours as her mother oversaw the morning rituals of dressing, making beds, cleaning rooms and making breakfast. Tiago walked to soccer practice at 9:30 while Renata and several friends went to school for a car wash. Paloma, with nowhere special to go, took her time finishing the pancakes that her grandmother had made from scratch, savoring the taste of the welcome alternative to frozen waffles.

"Can I work with you?" Paloma asked Elida as she entered the office after breakfast.

"Did you help Grandma do the dishes?"

"She said I didn't have to."

"O.K. then. Come, let's work together."

"Are you almost finished with your painting?" Paloma asked as she stood near Elida's easel, looking curiously at the painting.

"Almost. How do you like it?"

"I think the boy looks too sad."

"He is sad, in a way."

"Why?"

"Because he's not quite sure about the church. He sees that it's a beautiful building and he knows that inside things are peaceful and good. But outside, where he lives, things are not peaceful and good. His neighborhood is old and poor and dirty. He wonders why only the church is clean and pretty."

Paloma set up her easel which Elida had bought for her and she began to draw with markers. Her lines were precise and each shape was well-detailed although at first glance Elida could not make out what she was drawing.

"Don't look Mom," Paloma exclaimed. "Art takes time you know."

Elida laughed out loud which caught the attention of her mother who passed by the office.

"What are you doing Mom?" Elida asked.

"Oh, I just finished the dishes and I thought I'd go sit down and read a bit."

"Why don't you join us?"

Dora read quietly while her daughter and granddaughter worked diligently on their respective art projects. Paloma finished her drawing and began explaining it to Elida. She listened intently even though the drawing needed no explanation at all. In the middle of the drawing was a road. On one side of the road was a church, a small church with a short steeple. On the other side of the road was a house, a huge house with many windows. Standing in front of the house was a boy. He had a smile on his face larger than the house itself.

"Do you like it Mom?"

"I do, but that means that you don't like my painting."

"No, I like your painting. I just want the boy to be happy, that's all."

Paloma sat at her father's desk. She looked at her drawing over and over again. Elida continued with her painting and Dora continued to read. Paloma then began writing on a legal pad which she took from the top drawer of the desk. Occasionally she would leaf through her father's dictionary which she also took from the drawer. Elida watched curiously but didn't say a thing. Elida did ask however, what Paloma was up to when she folded the piece of paper that she was writing on and put it inside an envelope, which she had found in another drawer.

"Paloma what are you doing? You know you shouldn't be in your father's desk, especially when he's not home."

"I'm not doing anything Mom."

"Of course you're doing something. Did you write a letter to someone?"

Before Paloma could answer, although she had little intention of doing so, the telephone rang.

Elida grabbed the phone quickly and paused a second as the connection delayed. It was Orpet, calling long distance from Switzerland.

"Yes, yes, I can hear you dear; how are you?"

"I'm fine," Orpet replied from the bedside phone of his hotel in Geneva. "It's beautiful here Elida, very beautiful."

Dora set her book down and listened to one half of the conversation. Elida walked with the phone to the window and Paloma followed her closely.

"Let me talk Mom."

"Wait Paloma, it's long distance, just wait."

"I want to talk, now!" Paloma said again in a much too abrasive way.

"Just a second Orpet. Paloma, you wait. Run to the kitchen and get me a glass of water and you can talk when you get back."

Paloma did just as Elida had asked without realizing that Elida had wanted her out of the room.

"I don't know Orpet," Elida continued into the phone. "Things are crazy around here. I'm concerned."

"What do you mean?" Orpet asked.

"Paloma's been so nervous and it's making everything so uneasy. She's fine, I mean it's nothing serious, but she's acting strange, she's acting nervous."

"Elida if she's misbehaving you have to punish her. You

can't let her misbehave."

"She's not misbehaving Orpet. She's uneasy and nervous. I can see it. She's different and I'm concerned. I know Paloma and I know..."

Paloma returned to the office with a tall glass of water which she placed on the floor at Elida's feet.

"Let me talk to Daddy," she insisted.

Elida handed Paloma the phone and stood with her back against the window. She wiped her eyes with the tips of her fingers and breathed an unusually deep breath.

"Daddy, I want you to bring me back something from Switzerland."

"What is it Paloma?"

"A comb."

"A comb?" Orpet asked curiously. "Well, I don't know if Switzerland specializes in combs but I can look."

"I need a comb Daddy."

"I'll bring you a comb Paloma, I promise, but you be good, you hear? Don't give your Mom any trouble."

"Dad...I love you."

Paloma handed the phone to Elida and skipped out of the room. As Elida began to talk again, Paloma ran back into the office, picked up the envelope that she had prepared on Orpet's desk and ran back out again.

"I will, I will Orpet," Elida repeated into the phone. "I love you too. Come home soon."

"Relax Elida," Dora said as her daughter hung up the phone. "You're thinking too much, worrying too much. You need to relax a bit."

Elida didn't answer. She wiped her eyes again with the tips of her fingers and walked out of the office.

"I'll relax Mom," she said softly as she turned back inside the door.

Elida slumped onto the pillows of her bed and rolled around a bit. She picked up the book on her night stand and sat upright against the pillows which she rearranged. She turned to page 17 which was marked by several pieces of paper that were neatly folded inside the book. She set the book down and read from those pieces of paper first.

"Mom, desperately I loved you forever..."
"When you die I'll never forget you..."
"Nobody loves me.
"And if I'm not loved by anyone for what did I exist?"
"I'm going to die any day in my infancy."

She folded the pieces of paper along the lines of their original folds and tucked them carefully back inside the book. As she did, she glanced again at the passage that sat elegantly and boldly on page 17.

You are the bow from which your children as living arrows are sent forth.
The archer sees the mark upon the path of the infinite, and He bends you with His might that His arrow may go swift and far.
Let your bending in the archer's hand be for gladness...

Tiago and Renata came home within minutes of each other, just after 1:00, and both were starving. They also were filthy so Elida sent them to the showers while she promised to whip up a good lunch. Elida turned the radio in the kitchen on loud, very loud, as if the music would drown out whatever she was thinking and feeling. It seemed to work. She danced around the stove and didn't seem to mind as the grease from the French fries she was frying splattered all around. She took a package of lean ground beef out of the refrigerator, peeled off the plastic wrapping and placed it on the counter.

As the radio continued sending shock waves through the

kitchen, Elida sliced a few tomatoes, washed off some lettuce and tossed some paper plates onto the table. She danced her way outside and nearly tripped over Wolf in the process. The gas grill sat on the far end of the yard near the pool so it took Elida, even with her sudden burst of energy, a few minutes to get there. That was all the time Wolf needed.

Knowing exactly where he was going and what he was doing, Wolf put his nose inside the kitchen door, nudged it just enough for it to open and in he went. Within seconds the entire package of ground beef was gone. And within just a few more seconds, Wolf had slipped back into the yard and underneath a tree not far from Elida. She lit the gas grill without knowing that there was nothing left to grill.

"Damn it!" she screamed loud enough to drown out the radio when she returned to the kitchen. Tiago and his grandmother came running immediately to see what had happened and Renata, still in a towel and with her head dripping wet, soon followed. Elida sat down at the kitchen table and dejectedly put her face into her hands. Dora picked up the remains of the plastic wrapping from the floor and waved it angrily at Wolf who sat quietly and innocently just outside the kitchen door.

"Renata," Elida asked, "does that pizza place near your school deliver?"

It did, so Elida ordered a large cheese pizza to go along with cold French fries. Tiago set the paper plates in the living room while Renata popped a video tape into the VCR.

"Where's Paloma?" Elida asked as she served the pizza.

"I think she's in her room Mom," Renata answered as she bit into the steaming hot pizza. Elida set her plate down and walked to the bedroom. Paloma sat at her desk under a dim light, writing.

"Paloma come have pizza with us."

"I'm coming Mom. I'll be right there."

"You're writing again? What are you writing, a book?"

"No, not a book Mom. It's nothing. I'll be right there."

Elida left the room and began walking down the hallway when she heard an angry scream.

"Damn it!" Paloma's voice echoed throughout the house.

"What is it Paloma?" Elida asked as she returned to the room.

"My pencil. I can't find my pencil."

"Just look for it Paloma."

"I did look for it. I had it right here and now I can't find it."

"Calm down Paloma. Stop screaming."

"I can't find my pencil!"

"What's going on?" Renata asked as she entered the bedroom with the crust of her piece of pizza in her hand. "Why the screaming?"

"I can't find my pencil. I know it's here."

"Paloma stop screaming!"

"Mom, Paloma, both of you calm down."

Renata walked towards Paloma's desk, got down on her hands and knees and reached under the desk. She pulled out the pencil and handed it to her sister. "There you are Paloma. There's your pencil."

"Thank you Renata. Thank you so much."

"You're welcome Paloma," Renata said as she walked out of the bedroom and returned to the living room. Elida stood near the doorway, quiet and somewhat puzzled.

"Gosh Mom," Paloma said in reference to the incident. "Renata found my pencil so easily. It's almost as if she was my mother and you were my sister."

Elida said nothing in return. She was upset, confused and anxious.

She managed to rest in the afternoon while Renata, Tiago and eventually Paloma watched two movies on the VCR. It was rest that she would desperately need as the night ahead would provide no further rest at all.

The night was cool and a swift wind tapped continuously

on the window panes of every bedroom. Elida lay alone in her bed, longing for Orpet's company. She pulled the covers up around her neck and turned the last light in the house off when immediately she was shaken by a piercing scream.

"Mommy! Mommy!" Paloma screamed out from her bedroom in a desperate voice. Elida raced to the bedroom and flipped on the light.

"What is it Paloma? What's wrong?"

"I can't sleep Mom."

"But it's late Paloma, you have to sleep, you have school tomorrow."

"I can't sleep Mom. Let me come to your bed."

"Were you sleeping at all?" Elida asked as they walked down the hallway. "Did you dream anything?"

"No. I didn't sleep and I didn't dream."

Paloma climbed into her parent's bed and cuddled close to Orpet's pillow. Elida pulled the covers up around her neck and tucked her soft, silky hair against the pillow.

"Close your eyes and sleep Paloma."

"Mom, can you drive me to school tomorrow?"

"Paloma, I drove you twice last week. You can take the bus. Now, go to sleep."

"No Mom, I don't want to take the bus. I don't like it."

"Sleep Paloma, we'll talk about the bus tomorrow."

"Mom, can we pray?"

Elida lifted her head from her pillow and looked down at Paloma in pleasant disbelief. Paloma never wanted to pray with her at night. She kissed Paloma on the cheek and smiled.

"Yes, let's pray."

Paloma started softly and Elida joined her, but only for a moment.

She listened more than she spoke and was impressed by Paloma's prayer.

"Dear God, before I go to bed, please hear my last prayer. Thank you for all your help today and forgive me for any wrong

I did. I am truly sorry. Keep in your care my mother, my father, my brother, my sister, my grandmother and everyone I love. May the souls of the faithful departed, through the mercy of God, rest in peace. Amen,"

"Good night Mom." Paloma whispered.

"Good night Paloma."

Though the night was peaceful, Elida did not sleep. She lay close to Paloma who tossed and turned feverishly all night long. As the morning sun poked through the bedroom window, Paloma was the first to roll out of bed. She stumbled, actually, as she got out of bed and went to the bathroom. She was tired and she looked irritated. Elida was tired too and seeing Paloma irritated made her irritated as well.

"Mom, can you fix some breakfast for the kids? Elida asked Dora in the hallway. "I have to get dressed and go. I won't have time for breakfast."

"It's already on the table Elida. Come, have some coffee. You'll feel better."

Elida agreed and she did feel a bit better as she sipped from a fresh cup of coffee at the kitchen table. Tiago was the first to join her for breakfast and he quickly went to work on the fried eggs that his grandmother had prepared.

"You know Renata and I each have half-day today," he told Elida.

"I know," she said. "I'll probably be at the construction site when you get home and then I'm going straight to Paloma's school. Just come home and start your homework. You have a key, don't you?"

"Yes, I have a key."

"Why are you going to Paloma's school again Mom?" Renata asked as she entered the kitchen and poured herself a glass of orange juice.

"Just to give her a ride home. She doesn't like taking the bus for some reason."

"Gosh Mom," Renata said as she sat down at the table,

"you're going to drive out of your way to her school just because she doesn't like to take the bus."

"Renata, please..." Elida said quickly and then stopped as Paloma walked into the kitchen. Her eyes were weary but her hair, Elida noticed, was particularly shiny and clean. She stroked Paloma's hair a few times as she pushed in her chair at the kitchen table.

"Do you want an egg Paloma?" Dora asked. "I can make one up real fast if you'd like."

"No thank you Grandma, I'll just have some bread."

"Anyway," Renata said, "you know we have a half-day today Mom."

"I know," Elida replied. "Would you mind helping your grandmother with lunch today Renata?"

"Sure, what are we having? Not ground beef I hope."

"Funny, very funny," Elida said as Tiago laughed softly to himself.

Elida had a second cup of coffee as Dora poured herself a second cup. Tiago and Renata finished eating, cleared their plates and raced off to their bus stop. Elida watched them carefully and thought to herself how fortunate she was. They were good kids. She should have let them know that before they left she thought.

Paloma sat quietly in between her mother and grandmother and picked at her bread.

"Your hair is so soft and silky today sweetie," Elida said. "I don't think I've ever seen it so lovely. You look beautiful, as if you're going to a party."

Paloma gave a half-smile and picked at her bread some more. Elida got up from the table and made some toast for herself. She passed some butter over the bread quickly and sat back down to eat it with her coffee.

"Well, let's get going Paloma," Elida said as she finished and got up once more. "If you want me to drive you we have to leave now."

Elida warmed up the car in the driveway as Dora finished lacing the back of Paloma's pink dress. It was a sunny but cool morning and Paloma felt a small chill as she left the house and walked to the car. She waved at Dora and then blew her a kiss. It seemed so very simple for Dora. Every day, every moment, she was so patient and loving and understanding. Elida often wondered how, as a widow, her mother could be so pleasant and agreeable all the time. Life for her was not sad or bitter. Life went on and that was all. Losing her husband, Elida's father, was painful for sure, but Dora managed to move on and make the most of each day. Maybe she should learn a bit from her mother, Elida thought to herself as Paloma climbed into the car and sat in the back seat. Maybe she needed to learn.

"I'll be at your school right at 2:30," Elida told Paloma as they drove down the road and through the gate of the community. "Good morning Salvador," Elida yelled out of the window as they went.

"Don't be late Mom."

"I won't be late Paloma. Just wait on the steps and I'll be there."

"Thank you Mom," Paloma said sincerely.

Paloma stared blankly out of the window as they drove to school. Elida wanted to strike up some sort of conversation but the words just didn't come. Amazingly, she felt uncomfortable around Paloma again. They arrived at the school just seconds after the school bus and pulled in the driveway. Elida stopped the car just behind the bus and got out with Paloma. She ran her fingers through Paloma's hair and hugged her tightly.

"Paloma, you're so pretty," she said with a radiant smile. "How pretty you are. Have a good day Paloma."

"Bye Mom, thank you."

"Hey you," Elida said with a grin, "how about a kiss?"

Paloma stopped on the first step of the school entrance. She gently pressed her fingers to her lips and then blew her mother a kiss. She then turned and made her way up the rest of the steps and out of Elida's sight.

Elida drove straight to the construction site of their house to meet with the general contractor. The house was coming together quickly and Elida enjoyed the opportunity to get her mind off of her concerns about Paloma for a while. She stayed at the house and worked with the contractor for several hours.

"Elida, what happened?" Dora asked as Elida raced into the kitchen. "I thought you were going directly to Paloma's school."

"I was Mom. But I got tied up out at the house and then realized I forgot something here so I'm late, but I'm going."

Without even stopping for a moment, Elida picked up the dry cleaning receipt which she had forgotten and raced out of the house again. She put the key in the ignition and turned but there was silence. She turned it again. Nothing. The car wouldn't start. It always starts she thought to herself. What is going on? "What the hell is going on?" she screeched.

Elida rushed back into the house, right past Dora and grabbed the phone. She called the school and feverishly pleaded that someone get a message to Paloma to tell her to get on the bus home because her mother was having car problems. She pleaded that they tell Paloma this gently.

Elida hung up the phone and went back to the car to see the problem again. She pumped the pedal one more time and turned the key. It sputtered a few times and then started.

"I can't believe it," she screamed.

"What now?" Dora asked.

"The stupid thing started. I'm going to drive to the school and see if I can catch Paloma in time. I'll be right back Mom."

Elida sped nervously out of the driveway, down the road past the tennis courts and through the main gate.

"Slow down honey."

"Sorry Salvador."

She reached the school in nearly half the time it normally

took but as she pulled into the parking lot, she saw the golden mini bus pulling out at the far exit. The front steps of the school were empty so obviously Paloma had gotten on the bus. Elida buried her head in the steering wheel and banged on the dashboard.

"Stupid car. God, I hate this day."

She spun the car out of the parking lot and raced home just as quickly so as not to miss Paloma again. The bus made one stop before their community so she managed to get home ahead of time, pulling back into the driveway as the parents began congregating at the bus stop.

"You missed her at school?" Dora asked Elida as she entered the house.

"Yes Mom, just barely. She's going to be so upset."

"What's going on Mom?" Renata asked.

"Nothing Renata. It has just been a lousy day. I'm going to the bus stop to get Paloma. I'll be right back."

Elida stepped slowly out of the house, exhausted and stressed. Her body slumped forward as she paced the 200 yards to the bus stop.

Paloma sat alone in the first row along the right side of the bus. Her head bounced back along the top of the seat as the motion of the bus, and the fact that she hadn't slept well the night before put her into a drowsy slumber. As Mr. Castro turned the bus off the main street and through the community gate, Paloma opened her eyes briefly and caught a glimpse of Salvador at the guard house. Her eyes shut again and her head continued to nod as the bus rolled forward down the winding road.

As the children behind Paloma recognized her stop ahead, they called for her to get up. Slowly and awkwardly she lifted her body off of the seat and into the aisle as the bus continued moving, her eyes still half closed and in a daze.

And then, in the most confusing, chaotic and incredulous few seconds, Paloma's weak and weary body fell forward. She extended her arm to break the fall and in so doing grabbed the lever that opens the door. Before Mr. Castro could even see what had happened right at his feet, Paloma stumbled down the steps and plunged head first onto the street.

Just a few yards away, Elida and the other parents watched in horrifying terror and disbelief as Paloma's body twisted clumsily on the ground.

Before their screams and agonizing outbursts had reached the ears of the driver, the back wheels of the bus brushed alongside her frail and fragile torso, pinning her to the concrete.

Elida let out a screeching and painfully shrill scream that reverberated throughout the normally quiet and peaceful surroundings of the community. Renata went out of the front door of the house and down the road as she heard the other mothers screaming madly as well. Elida lunged helplessly towards Paloma who lay motionless on the ground. The bus pulled to the side of the road and Mr. Castro leaped down the steps and collapsed by Elida's side. The children scurried off the bus but were steered away from the scene by the frantically anxious mothers. Within seconds, Salvador had driven his car down the road in response to the turmoil.

"Oh my God," Elida screamed over and over again. "Paloma, my God, help, help!"

"Go call an ambulance!" Mr. Castro yelled to Salvador. "Now!"

"I can drive," Salvador said. "Put her in my car and let's go."

"Oh my God!" Elida continued as she cradled Paloma, and sobbed uncontrollably.

"Mom, what happened!" Renata screamed, pulling her hair nervously as she watched her sister squirming on the ground.

"Get her to a hospital, now!" Mr. Castro insisted.

Several mothers lifted Elida to her feet as Mr. Castro and Salvador grasped Paloma gently and raised her off the ground.

"Let go of me!" Elida screamed, swinging her arms wildly. "Give me my daughter!"

The mothers led her to the back seat of the car and she held Paloma in her arms. Renata jumped in the car of a neighbor who followed as Salvador sped off towards the city. A neighbor located Tiago and instructed him to stay home with his grandmother.

Salvador raced through two stop signs and nearly clipped a motorcyclist as he flew through a red light. Elida closed her eyes tightly and shook her head. As she opened them again, she noticed Paloma's eyes slowly opening.

"Did I die yet Mom?" Paloma asked in a faintly audible utterance.

"No sweetie. My God, you're not going to die."

"I am Mommy. I'm going to die."

"No Paloma. I'm taking you to the hospital."

"No Mommy. I'm going to die. I'm going to die."

Paloma moved slowly in Elida's grip and grimaced in pain. Elida glanced frightfully out of the window and then back at Paloma. There was no blood but Paloma's midsection, where the huge tires of the bus had struck, gurgled grotesquely. She continued moaning while her eyes moved aimlessly about her head.

Elida caressed her shiny hair and began softly singing a hymn that she remembered from church. Paloma's eyes focused on the sounds of the mother's voice. "Jesus loves me...that I know...."

"Don't sing Mommy.... Don't sing...."

Elida stopped immediately and looked down at Paloma in further disbelief. Paloma closed her eyes and lay still.

Salvador drove like a maniac to the front of the Emergency Room entrance and slammed on the brakes of the car. He got out, opened Elida's side and with the assistance of an attendant at the hospital, gently lifted Paloma and took her into the hospital.

"Wait for me! Paloma! Wait for me."

Moments later, inside the hospital corridor, Renata grabbed Elida's left hand and stopped her from running. They embraced each other, burying their heads on each other's shoulders. A nurse quickly brought over a wheelchair and sat Elida down.

"Please be calm. The doctors are with your daughter right now. The Emergency Room is just at the end of the hall."

Renata moved her mother close to the wall and stood next to her firmly, holding her hand tighter than perhaps she even could.

"She'll be O.K. Mom. She just hurt her stomach, but she'll be O.K."

"My God, how could this happen?" Elida continued through her still uncontrollable tears. "She didn't want to take that damn bus. And my damn car let her down!"

"Mommy, please. She'll be O.K. I know it."

Elida banged nervously on the wheelchair and stared helplessly down the hallway which was bustling with activity. Suddenly she remembered Orpet who was miles and miles away, totally unaware of what was happening. Nothing in the family ever happened without him, she thought to herself. He was always there, the rock that everyone could lean on.

She remembered how strong and brave he was when Renata fell off the swing in school and nearly fractured her spine. He controlled that situation, comforted and assured everyone that Renata would be all right. Elida distinctly remembered the hug she gave him when the doctors said that there was no serious injury at all.

She continued to bang on the wheelchair, wishing he was there to bang on instead.

Elida leaped to her feet as the door of the Emergency Room finally swung open. Renata, who stood strong and brave and hadn't shed a single tear while filling the role her father could not play, grabbed her mother by the arm and sat her down again. Three doctors in the most perfectly white uniforms that Elida had ever seen came walking down the hallway with their heads towards the floor. "My saviors," she thought to herself as she watched these polished, fine professionals walking towards her.

Her mind raced with anxiety as they approached. She waited for one of them to say something. But there was silence, cold silence. The tall doctor in the middle then slowly raised his head and somehow gained the courage to look Elida right in the eyes. He shook his head.

Paloma was dead.

Chapter 12

The operator at the Hotel Beau-Rivage in Geneva let the phone ring in room 421 six times before telling one of Orpet's Navy colleagues who came to the house that there was nobody in the room.

"Please try again, it's extremely important." he said in his best possible English.

"Sir, I'm sure that there's no one in the room at this time, but if you leave a message I'll be sure to mark it urgent for him."

"That'll be fine, thank you."

Renata grabbed the phone in the kitchen on the first ring as her uncle called from Rio.

"Where's your mother Renata?"

"She's here, but I don't think she can talk on the phone."

"I know, that's O.K. Who else is there?"

"Tiago and my grandmother are here of course. A few neighbors are here. Salvador, the guy who works at the guard house is here plus a few people I don't even know. It's real confusion here you know."

"I'm sure. Just be strong honey and help your mother as best you can. Some of the family members here in Rio will be driving to São Paulo soon to be with you, O.K.?

"Yes. O.K."

Orpet was in the lobby of the luxurious Hotel Beau-Rivage waiting for some colleagues. He had spent a free day touring some local spots like the Jet d'Eau, the Flower Clock in the Jardin Anglais and the Left Bank's Old Town. He ate only some fruit and cheese for lunch at a small cafe, saving himself for a more elaborate Swiss dinner. Without even a clue of what had happened only hours before back home in São Paulo, he remarked to the first colleague who joined him in the lobby what a truly pleasant and beautiful day it had been so far. Two other gentlemen, both from France, met up with Orpet and the colleague from England and the four of them walked outside to wait for a cab.

Elida stumbled out of the front door and grabbed the wooden post of the porch for support. The evening air chilled her already shivering body. She looked out at the driveway and saw her car parked innocently. She cursed it with her eyes and then turned her head away from it quickly. She followed the line of trees down the road to the bus stop where not even a trace of what had happened that afternoon remained. As her eyes wandered, she realized how calm and peaceful the surroundings had become. A few seconds later, however, she batted her eyes and shook her head and recalled exactly what had happened. Paloma had died. There was no peace at all.

On Rua Campo Sales in Rio, Lourdes threw some clothes into a small bag while two of her children organized the house quickly.

"How could this have happened?" Lourdes asked, crying desperately between each word. "My God, can you imagine?"

"And with Orpet out of the country," her daughter added. "Nothing in that family ever happens without Orpet being involved. But this happens. I can't believe it."

"How is Orpet possibly going to fly home knowing that Paloma is gone?"

For the time being Orpet still did not know. He sat around a large table in an exquisite French style restaurant on Geneva's Right Bank. Swiss meals are frequently long drawn out affairs and this one had been exactly that. The filet of perch from Lake Geneva that Orpet ordered was the most delicious fish he ever remembered eating.

He entered the lobby of the Beau-Rivage and went immediately to his room. As soon as he entered, he saw the flashing red lights on the telephone. He went into the bathroom to wash his face and as the cold water splashed against his hands, he figured that his plans for the next day were being changed again and that it was a member of the Navy back in São Paulo calling to let him know. He toweled off his hands and face and picked up the phone.

"Yes please, this is room 421. I have a message?"

He waited patiently on the phone for an instant as the hotel operator went to check on the message. When the operator returned and told him the number to call, he thanked her politely and hung up the phone. Before he could even stop and think of what it possibly could be, Orpet dialed his brother's number. It barely rang once at the other end.

"Hello."

"Hey it's me, I just got your message. What's up?"

"Orpet! Jesus, where have you been?"

"Where have I been? Who is this, my brother or my mother?"

"Orpet, listen to me very carefully. Something bad has happened... with Paloma."

"What happened?"

"She got hurt."

"Where?"

"On the bus."

"How bad is it?"

"It's bad Orpet."

"Is it fatal?"

There was a pause and a huge lump came to Orpet's brother's throat. He thought for a moment that maybe it would be better if he didn't tell him exactly so that he'd be in a little better shape to fly home. He continued to pause. But Orpet, always so smart and cunning and aware, had asked such a direct question. No one could hide anything from

Orpet or even attempt a lie. He would know. Besides, why would he have to fly home from an important business trip if it wasn't that important. He took one big deep breath.

"Yes, it's fatal."

There was a long silence. Orpet squeezed the phone in his hand and pushed it into his neck. With his other hand he grabbed the top of his head and squeezed that too. A sharp pain came to his head, matching the one deep in his stomach. At the other end of the phone, Orpet's brother closed his eyes and prayed that he had done the right thing. He wasn't sure. Finally, he spoke softly.

"Orpet...?"

"I heard you...I'll be on the next flight."

A sliver of the pale gray moon dangled in the nighttime sky and cast an ominous glow upon the golf course. The temperature had dropped steadily and the tiny black bird that fluttered its wings on a branch and took to the air did so in an apparent search for a warm place to spend the night.

Elida spotted the bird as it soared high above the row of eucalyptus trees and she immediately remembered Paloma and the day they prayed for another bird. She walked away from the house and out onto the cool grass of the fairway. Her tired legs then buckled and she fell, burying her face and her tears in the grass.

"Mom! What happened?" Renata screamed as she saw her mother from the porch and went running after her. "Mom, please!"

Renata lifted her mother to her feet and wrapped her arms around her shoulders. Slowly the two continued walking under the guidance of the faint moonlight.

"Mom, what can we do?"

"I don't know Renata, I don't know."

"I can't believe she died Mom. Just like that, she died."

"I don't know Renata, I don't know anything."

The row of eucalyptus trees on the fairway stood as they

always had before. Just as Elida had admired them in the past, the trees never changed despite the changes around them. Orpet was far away, Paloma was even farther away and yet the trees stood as if everything was in its proper order.

The yellow taxi cab sped through the streets of Geneva as fast as it could but Orpet demanded that the cab driver do better. Without any of his papers or suitcases or thoughts in order, Orpet had little idea of how he was going to get back to Brazil. The driver assured him that there would be flights at least to London or Paris and that they would be at the airport in just a matter of minutes. Orpet told the cab driver that there were no such things as assurances.

They did arrive at the Geneva-Cointrin Airport in just a few minutes and Orpet raced out of the cab and into the airport. He forced his way to the front of the line at the counter. There was a flight to London boarding in fifteen minutes, from there he would find his way to São Paulo. Orpet slammed his passport and his suitcases and a credit card on the counter and without wasting any time talking to an agent, demanded the immediate attention of an authority. He quickly explained the emergency and minutes later walked away with a boarding pass.

He began running down the hallway to the gate when suddenly he stopped in his tracks in front of a gift shop. He entered the store and began pacing nervously. A woman stood behind the register and watched just as nervously.

"May I help you?" she asked first in French and then in English.

"No, I'm just looking for something," Orpet replied in English.

He paced back and forth along the aisles of the store as the woman kept watching.

"Please sir, let me help you find what you're looking for."

Orpet did not answer as the woman stepped out from behind the register and began following him, cautiously observing what she now assumed to be either a shoplifter or a lunatic. She then shouted out to him in disapproval as he walked behind the cash register.

"Sir! Get out of there or I'll call security."

"I found it," Orpet said as he reached his hand into a glass container on a shelf behind the cash register.

"A comb?" the woman asked curiously.

"Yes, I need to buy this comb."

Chapter 13

Angelic. Not even in life had her beauty been so evident. It was as if death had uplifted not only her spirit, but her entire being as well.

Her long blonde hair was shiny and brimming with an energizing glow. Her cream colored face was unblemished and pure. She was a portrait of magnificence and grace.

She resembled a brand new porcelain doll in the window of an expensive toy store. But just like the doll's, her delicate beauty was now only cosmetic and superficial. Inside was emptiness; no heart, no soul and no life.

The tears and agonizing sighs of grief were uncontrollable as family members and close friends passed in front of the coffin to see Paloma's face for the last time. Aside from Elida, who was too weak and too broken to even stand, it was the children who seemed to suffer most. And the adults, unable to provide any reason or explanation for the fatal departure of Paloma, were little comfort. Death had invaded their family with such a sudden and impetuous force that no one was able to fill the void, at least not yet.

Renata and Tiago sat close to their parents, silent and distant. The other children wept feverishly as they cautiously walked in front of the open casket. From the back of the church came a constant, high-pitched cry of immense pain and suffering. It was Auxiliadora. She would soon excuse herself and go outside where she crumbled to the ground, clutching and tearing at the blades of grass on the church lawn.

The grandmothers, Dora and Lourdes, those who in the

natural scheme of life's progression are supposed to die first, stood together, just a few feet from their fallen granddaughter. Both agreed that there was nothing worse than a death that went against the grain of a normal chronology and as mothers they both agreed that there could be nothing more painful or more crushing to the spirit than for a mother to lose a child. That Paloma was taken just eight short years after Elida had brought her into the world made the reality all the more horrendous for everyone.

Elida slumped further into Orpet's arms as that reality continued pounding inside her head. Also rattling her mind as she stared blankly at the floor were vivid flashes of the school bus that had brought on all this suffering and grief. As she lifted her head and looked toward Paloma, she tried to turn her thoughts to the moments they had spent together but the school bus was all that she could see.

She wailed hysterically despite the efforts of those around her to calm and comfort her. And then suddenly, as though she were a kettle of water that had reached its boiling point, Elida stood up, lunged towards the coffin and began screaming.

"No! No God! Don't take Paloma! Please don't take Paloma from me! Take us together God!"

Tiago arose from his seat and grabbed his mother from behind, holding her back as she stumbled towards the coffin.

"Mom, don't say that! We need you Mom! Please Mom, we need you!"

Renata got her mother by the waist and helped Tiago lead her out of the church.

"Wait for me!" Elida screamed back in the direction of the coffin. "Wait for me Paloma! Wait for me!"

Orpet, equally drained from the ordeal as from the long and lonely plane ride back from Europe, remained seated in the pew as the church gradually emptied out. He had said very little except for expressing his disbelief at how such an accident could have happened in their quiet neighborhood and how a supposedly safe school bus with a qualified driver could have allowed such an unbelievable mishap. He angrily and firmly made clear his intention to meet with members of the school board to get an explanation, an issue that Elida had paid little attention to considering the priorities of the situation. There was no bringing Paloma back. Not even Orpet, who could accomplish everything, could do that.

Having always walked with an air of confidence and certainty, Orpet managed to display only hesitancy and timidity as he approached the coffin. No words came to him as he stood before Paloma. Instead, he quietly and intently stared straight through her, wondering what had gone wrong and why he was able to do nothing. A rare tear fell from his eye and slipped gently down his cheek. He had let Paloma down; he thought to himself. He wasn't there for her. Being there for his family was his responsibility and he had failed. He felt an awful, shallow cavity inside of him. He began to cry even more.

He reached into the breast pocket of his jacket and slowly pulled his hand back out. As a few members of the family stood in the back of the church watching with equal amounts of concern and curiosity, Orpet pulled from his pocket a simple but fine silver comb. He clutched Paloma's hand and carefully placed the comb in her palm.

"Here is your comb Paloma, just as Daddy promised."

Still crying and now shaking a bit, Orpet stood holding his daughter's hand. He looked straight at her beautiful face. Orpet, the businessman and mathematician and pragmatist had seen death before this moment without a human face. Now, as he held Paloma's hand and touched the comb and looked at her face, he not only saw, but experienced the pain of loss with a human face. He wiped away his tears and smiled at his fallen angel.

As he walked away from the coffin and towards the back of

the church, he heard the sweet sounds of music playing in the sanctuary. He stopped and sat down, alone, to listen for a while longer. Renata and Tiago came looking for their father and they sat with him when they found him. He moved between them and put his arms around each one.

"Where's your mother?" he asked quietly.

"She's outside with everyone else," Renata answered. "She's in bad shape Dad."

"I know she is. I know. Why don't we go."

Orpet led his two children, now, outside into the warm sunshine of another glorious day in Brazil. The warmth of the sun felt good on his tired body. Family members huddled around each other, clinging to whatever each could get or give to another. Orpet found Elida and he swiftly ushered her off towards the car.

The day was long and the night was longer. The house was cold and dark and empty, empty of life, that is. Orpet, Elida, Renata, Tiago and Dora were there, but it was still empty. Elida sat in Paloma's room, at the edge of her bed. The pink curtains were drawn allowing only a faint bit of moonlight to enter. What did enter helped illuminate the shelf where Paloma's ponies stood in perfect order. Elida stared straight at them. They could not know of the void that had been created. They could not know that the fine silver comb that was intended for them would not be arriving. She could not tell them that the sweet and gentle hand that had stroked their manes so many times before would never do so again. She could not tell them that the loving, caring little girl who nurtured and pampered them in the past would never do so again. She could not convince herself of these sad truths, so how could she possibly get these innocent ponies to understand? There was no explanation, at least not yet.

Chapter 14

In the weeks that followed, Elida disappeared, mentally and emotionally. Although he suffered just as much, Orpet got up every day and went to work, trying his best to concentrate on the intense demands of the Navy's projects. As painful as it was for them, Renata and Tiago got up every day and went to school. Elida went into virtual seclusion.

She would sit in Paloma's room, amongst her things, and cry. She withdrew further and further from her own life and the life of her family. She thrust herself into a whirlwind of contemplation, yet she found nothing but pain and sadness as the days passed.

She managed to find some peace and comfort alone in the church. She was overwhelmed with guilt for not being closer to the church. She was angry at herself for having forgotten about the church and about prayer while she became consumed with things like houses and paintings and dinners out. All she wanted, as she sat in an empty pew during the earliest Mass on a Sunday morning, was to hold Paloma close to her and pray. Elida sat up straight in the pew and looked around. It was too late.

"Oh, God, help me," she said quietly to herself. "Forgive me for coming to you only in my time of need. I know I should have been closer all along. Perhaps I am guilty of going astray, but if so, what is the incentive to change now? Paloma is gone."

In another church, miles away in Belo Horizonte in the state of Minas Gerais, Orpet's cousin, Heloisa, stood before the altar. A teeming rain pounded the streets outside while an angry wind wreaked additional havoc against the walls of the church. Heloisa had battled the rain and the wind to help a group of women volunteers decorate the church. The women's work had already begun as Heloisa shook herself dry at the door and then walked towards the altar. As she worked, she prayed silently for Paloma.

High above the expansive sanctuary on the wall behind the altar was the crucifix, grand and magnificent. Heloisa raised her head from time to time to look reverently at the figure of Christ and then repeatedly closed her eyes to concentrate solely on Paloma.

Also grand and magnificent, coming from high above the church to the rear, were the sounds of the organ that rang out with a boldness of an intense spirit. Heloisa had forgotten just how powerful and moving the components of the church were and in her prayers she apologized for being so aloof.

She also apologized in her prayers to Orpet and Elida, apologized for being so distant before it was too late. The memories she had of Paloma from a brief visit to Rio a long time ago were few. Her mind then raced in a fury throughout the family tree. She silently named each child as she pictured their faces and smiles and she planned the things she would do for each while the opportunity still existed. It was a frivolous exchange of ideas, she realized, and as she glanced upwards towards the crucifix again she returned her thoughts to Paloma and prayed more intensely for her well being.

The stained glass windows that adorned the church were void of any light as the dark clouds hovered over and around the church. The cool, damp air of the outside had crept into the church and left Heloisa feeling cold despite the warm vibrations surrounding her. Even the sweet and melodic sounds of the choir mixed with the tapping of the rain on the windows could not dispel her gloom, which Heloisa prayed would clear, both literally and figuratively.

As Heloisa worked at decorating the altar with flowers and

continued with her silent prayers, an older woman walked from the back of the church to the front and joined her.

"How are you?" the woman asked Heloisa as together they worked on the altar.

"Uh, I'm fine," Heloisa stuttered as she struggled to remember the woman's name. "I'm sorry, it's..."

"Maria," the woman said, "Maria da Costa."

"I'm sorry I didn't remember. Shamefully, I don't come to church as often as I should."

"I understand. Where are your boys today?"

"They're home; they didn't want to go out in the rain to help Mom at church, you know."

"And who was the little girl that you were with earlier?" Maria asked.

"What little girl?"

"I saw you walk in today with a lovely little girl. I'd never seen her before."

"I don't know what you're talking about."

"The girl. I saw you with a little girl in a white dress. I saw the two of you enter the church together."

"Maria, what color hair did this girl have, the girl that you saw with me?"

"Blonde. She had the most strikingly shiny, long blonde hair that I've ever seen on a little girl."

"Did you say blonde?"

"Yes, that's right."

"Maria, please excuse me. I have to go."

"God bless you dear," she said as Heloisa ran up the aisle towards the back of the church. "God bless you."

Outside the rain was coming down harder and Heloisa was drenched by the time she reached her car. She sped through the slick, rain-drenched streets to her house and stormed into the kitchen, and managed to leave the front door open to the wind and the rain. She grabbed her personal phone book off the counter and as she looked up Elida's phone number, she cursed herself for not knowing it by heart.

"Elida, believe me," Heloisa said nervously as she recounted the story. "I wouldn't make something like this up."

"I know you wouldn't."

"It was so strange."

"But Heloisa, this woman never saw Paloma."

"And I barely know the woman Elida. That's what I'm saying. It doesn't make any sense."

"And you say she saw you with a little girl?"

"Yes, she came up to me and asked me about the girl I was with. I was alone, Elida. The kids were here at home. I went by myself. The woman had some kind of vision. I thought she was crazy, one of these religious lunatics. But then she described Paloma exactly. I nearly fainted."

"I don't know what to say Heloisa," Elida said through a stream of tears that dampened the telephone. "I've been praying a lot, praying for some type of an explanation, but I don't know what to say about this."

"Elida, I shouldn't even try to say anything to you because I know there's no way I can relate to what you're experiencing. I'm no theologian and I'm not a serious Catholic or anything. But this is clearly a message Elida. Paloma's spirit is alive. She was in our church today."

Orpet listened carefully as Elida recounted the story to him that evening in the office. He listened, but it didn't necessarily register anywhere special. Though he decided not to pursue any type of an investigation with the bus driver, he wasn't about to turn full cycle and believe that Paloma's death was anything more than an accident.

"You know, speaking of my cousin," he said to Elida as she gazed out the office window, "everyone in the family has really been considerate. We really ought to send out some notes of thanks."

"I know we should, you've reminded me of that three times this week."

"Well, it's been six weeks since the funeral."

"So you expect my feelings to operate according to the calendar?"

"No, I just..."

"Damn it Orpet! What do you want from me? Do you want me to wake up every morning and go about my business as if nothing ever happened?"

"No, I..."

"Maybe you can do that. Maybe you're that strong. And you have your job to deal with, your bills to pay, and your investments to take care of. You can get on with your life. I can't. I have nothing. Paloma was my life. And now she's gone. She's dead. And I feel dead too. To hell with the thank you notes, O.K.?"

"Elida, please," Orpet said as he walked towards his wife at the window. He held her with both hands in front of him. "I know what you're going through. I feel the same things, maybe I just don't show it. And maybe I don't think some of the same things that you do. But I feel them. I know it's hard. I was just trying to think of the family and how good they've been to us."

"I'm sorry Orpet. I didn't mean to yell at you. I just hurt so much. I don't know what to do."

She fell into his arms and buried her crying eyes in his chest.

"We have to hold it together honey."

"I want to send out the thank you notes Orpet, but I don't want to send out just anything. I want to send a message that people can remember Paloma by and something that'll help them understand her the way we do and help them understand what all this has meant. God will help me find the right words. I pray that he will."

Elida continued to pray, day after day. She sat on the patio in the backyard with Wolf at her feet and sifted through the Bible in search of something to write to the family. She found several items that seemed to pertain to Paloma and to the fact that this was somehow an act of God, or of destiny. She wasn't sure and she hesitated to take on the role of a preacher to the family. She closed the Bible and buried her head between her knees, feeling weak and helpless once again.

Elida walked aimlessly through the house; she felt weaker as she sat in front of the computer. A twinge grasped her body and without knowing why, she opened the top drawer of the desk. There, underneath a pencil was a white piece of paper, folded in half.

Elida's heart began beating wildly.

She grabbed the piece of paper in her hand and raced out of the office towards Paloma's room. She entered quickly and then stopped dead in her tracks. The room was empty and silent which caused Elida to drop to the floor in despair. She lifted herself onto Paloma's bed and after pausing a while to find an ounce of energy, she slowly and nervously unfolded the note.

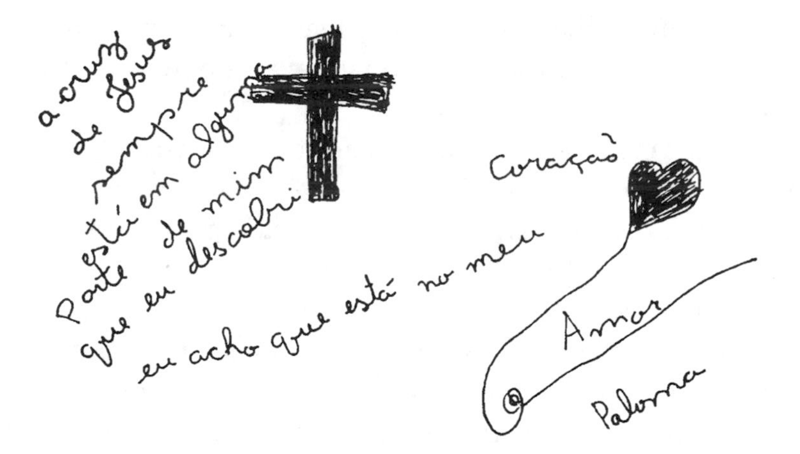
a cruz
de Jesus
sempre
está em alguma
parte de mim
que eu descobri
eu acho que está no meu
Coração
Amor
Paloma

"the cross of Jesus
is always in some part of me
I discovered
I think it is in my heart
Love
Paloma"

Elida fell back onto the bed and looked to the ceiling and then to the pink curtains over the window. Tears streamed down her face and she let out an agonizing sigh. Orpet came running from the kitchen and lifted his wife into his arms.

"What is it Elida? What happened?"

Elida handed the paper to Orpet who read it several times before trying to respond.

"Elida, this is amazing."

"No, Orpet, this is a miracle. This is a miracle between God and our daughter."

Elida walked to the office and sat down at her easel, the first time she had done so since Paloma's passing, and she began to sketch. She drew in childish, stick figure lines a simple drawing that she had adapted from a children's Mass book. She folded the paper in half and on the inside left she glued Paloma's note to the page. On the inside right she scripted a simple message to those dear people who extended so much comfort and love to them. She folded the paper and placed it inside an envelope. She then gave it to Orpet.

"Here you are Orpet, here's our thank you note. Take it to the printer and send it to the family."

She smiled at him and then looked to the ceiling.

"Thank you God," she whispered. "Thank you."

Deixai vir a mim as criancinhas porque
e delas o reino de Dues. (Mt. 19.14)

Let the children come to me...
for the kingdom of heaven
belongs to such as these.

Agradecemos a todos nossos amigos pelo apoio, conforto e demonstracao de carinho e amor para nos e nossa linda menina que partiu, mas que pela fe nos diz que vive feliz junto ao Senhor.
Orpet, Elida, Renata e Tiago

"We thank all of our friends for the support, comfort and demonstrations of love and tenderness towards us and towards our beautiful little girl who left us, but according to our faith, lives happily with the Lord."

Chapter 15

Elida's search for a reason had begun. Her pain and her immense suffering, created by the huge void that existed in her life, was transforming into an energy of faith and hope. She remained reclusive and indifferent to things going on around her but each day that energy got stronger and she got closer to the explanation that she needed

Orpet and Renata, both strong and independent, moved forward in their own positive way. Tiago had more trouble.

"He's so different now," Elida said to Orpet. "Haven't you noticed the change in him? He loved Paloma more than anything in this world. I know he's always been introverted and to himself, but he's withdrawn much more since she went away. Several times I've found him in his room crying into his pillow. He's suffering so. I think Tiago's childhood ended when Paloma left and that's such a shame."

"He'll be all right Elida," Orpet replied confidently. "All of us are going to be all right."

The completion of the new house and the preparations for moving were the distractions that everyone needed. Orpet worked busily with contractors, brokers and bankers to insure that everything would finish and close properly. Elida spent her time with decorators and designers. Renata and Tiago helped in any way that they could, especially with the packing.

Elida began packing her own bedroom, and as she did, she came across the contents of her night stand. She sat on the floor and read over and over again the notes that Paloma had written. Once again, she was thrust into a whirlwind of contemplation.

"Mom, desperately I loved you forever...
I will die any day during my infancy..."

How could an 8-year-old girl write such profound messages she thought to herself? Was it possible for her to predict her own fate? And how could her mother fail to heed the warnings that her daughter had put forth? Elida pondered those bewildering and painful questions and a sharp pain ran up her neck and pierced her head like a knife. She sat on the floor next to the night stand and held the notes tightly in her hands. She read them over and over again and as the pain in her head intensified, her eyes transfixed upon the words of one of them.

"...I loved you forever..."

"Loved!" Elida said out loud as she got up and walked to the window and looked out at the bright and sunny day. "Loved, not love," she said to herself over again.

Elida did not eat or sleep the rest of the day, nor did she talk to anyone. She just talked to herself, through the tears that streamed endlessly down her face. "Loved," she repeated, "Why loved?"

Dr. Wagner received Elida's call at his home just after 7:00 AM the next morning. Perhaps just as fatigued and stressed as his patient, Dr. Wagner agreed to meet with Elida within the hour. She drove quickly and nervously to the office and stood outside the door at 7:20 where she waited for another twenty minutes.

"I got here as soon as I could," the doctor apologized as he juggled with his key ring in order to open the door.

"I was going to call you last night," Elida said as she entered the office and sat herself down in the same chair that she had occupied for weeks. "I couldn't sleep at all but I figured at least I'd let you sleep."

"Appreciated, now what's the problem?"

Elida took the note from her purse and handed it to Dr. Wagner.

"She wrote these notes for me, I've shown many of them to you and we've talked about them. But I read this one again yesterday. Read it doctor."

"Mom, desperately I loved you forever..."

Dr. Wagner read the note slowly and quietly with his back straight and his head down.

"Every day I make love for you with the same words so that you will know that love is endless..."

"Stop!" Elida interrupted as she leaned forward on the doctor's oak desk. "Don't you see it?"

Dr. Wagner paused and stared blankly at Elida. He read the note again to himself and then looked again at Elida's anxious face.

"Can't you see it?" Elida pleaded.

"I don't know what you're getting at," he replied.

Elida got up from the chair and uncharacteristically approached Dr. Wagner on his side of the desk. She leaned over his shoulder and pointed to the first line of the note.

"Loved! She wrote it in the past tense doctor. She wrote 'Loved,' not love!"

The doctor fixed his eyes on the note again. Elida waltzed frantically around the office and then stopped near the door.

"She knew she was going to die, Dr. Wagner. She wrote to me in the past tense as if she was already dead. And now that I read the notes over again, it's as if she's writing them now."

Dr. Wagner remained silent as Elida's discovery made its

way into his mind. He shook his head in amazement.

"This is really something," he replied rather unprofessionally. "I've never in all my years come across anything as profound as this."

"Well that makes two of us," Elida said somewhat sarcastically and disparagingly as she took back the note from Dr. Wagner. "There is another explanation and I'm going to find it."

The house was exactly as Elida had first drawn it on her easel. It stood tall and proud on a cul de sac between two of the tallest eucalyptus trees in São Paulo. The walkway leading up to the solid oak door was adorned with bright flowers and finely trimmed bushes.

Inside, white ceramic tile graced the floor of an expansive living room. The bay window and the brick fireplace were in the precise location that Elida's blueprint had indicated. The glass windows to the yard were of the proper tint that she had ordered and the mirrors in the dining room gave the presence that she had predicted when she chose them.

As she walked throughout the house, a rare sense of joy and satisfaction overcame her. That feeling soon dissipated, however, as she found that there was something in the house that she had not predicted, one extra bedroom. Elida stood at the doorway of what was to be Paloma's bedroom. She looked out of the window and saw the sky. It was beautiful. She quickly wiped away a tear as she heard the noise of the van in the driveway.

"Let's get going Tiago," Orpet said as he hopped down from the van and opened up the back.

"Let me operate the dolly," Tiago said to his father as they prepared to unload the first items of the move.

"Hold on, I'll handle the heavy stuff first."

"Welcome home," Elida said with a half-smile as she greeted her husband in the driveway.

"Is everything all right?" he asked as he noticed the redness in her eyes.

"As good as it can be Orpet. Come, let's move in."

Orpet carefully maneuvered the washing machine on the dolly and led it into the garage. Elida directed him up the step and into the laundry room where the machine fit perfectly, just as she had planned. Orpet returned to the van with the dolly to start on the dryer while Tiago carried some boxes and trunks to the garage.

"Why don't I go back to the house and help Renata organize things there," Elida suggested to Orpet as he got the dryer in place.

"Are you sure you want to?"

"Yes, I have to."

The two movers drove ahead in the van as Elida drove alone in her car. She wound around the back roads slowly, letting her mind wander with each turn. Although she tried not to, she couldn't help but remember the day she drove hastily along the same road, trying desperately to catch Paloma before she got on the school bus.

She drove slowly through the gate which Fernando had opened for her. Salvador had left one week after Paloma's death. He tried to explain that he had found a better job in the city. Elida looked in his eyes and knew that the reason was not that.

At the old house, Elida began the task that she had put off for as long as she could. She entered Paloma's bedroom and slowly began going through her things to pack. She rummaged through the toys, toys that once were so active all throughout the house. She went over each piece of clothing, delicate fabrics that once covered her equally delicate little body.

Renata came into the room and put her hand on Elida's shoulder.

"I shared a lot of these things with Paloma you know."

"I know you did Renata. You are a good sister and you've

been a terrific young lady. I know I've been a lousy mother for you lately, just crying and crying day and night. I'm sorry."

"You don't ever have to apologize to me Mom. I know how much you loved Paloma. I know how sad you are. It's O.K. Don't worry about me."

"I love you so much Renata."

"I love you too Mom."

The two embraced in the middle of Paloma's bedroom as the sun radiated through the bright pink curtains onto their faces.

"Do you think it's possible Mom," Renata asked, "that Paloma's death really wasn't an accident? Do you think it happened for a reason, as part of some plan of sorts, some special purpose?"

"I'm really beginning to think so. When I think of everything that happened, and how it happened, it makes me believe that the finger of God was guiding Paloma and she knew it."

"It's so hard to accept, but maybe, if this is true, then there can be some comfort in it," Renata continued.

"Maybe you're right Renata, maybe you're right."

"I think I'll go to the garage and see what needs to be packed. Will you be all right Mom?"

"I will Renata. Thank you."

Elida got up from the edge of Paloma's bed and walked over to her desk. On top were several school papers of hers that Elida had seen before. She opened one drawer and fingered through a variety of odds and ends that Paloma had collected, items that Elida had also seen before.

In fact, as Elida recalled, she had been through the desk many times throughout her moments of desperation and despair. She opened another drawer; however, and found an envelope that she had not seen. She took the envelope from the drawer and walked to the window where she carefully opened it under the light of the day. Inside was a clean white piece of paper. She unfolded the paper and saw the all too familiar handwriting of Paloma.

coração criança Paloma criança coraçõa

Crer é verdade numa esperança ajente tem criação da vida

heart *child*
Paloma
child *heart*

"To believe is truth in a hope that
we have the creation of life"
Signed: Paloma

Elida's heart nearly burst inside and she felt a sharp pain all throughout her body. She grasped the note in her palm and looked out across the golf course. Three months after leaving, Paloma was still speaking to her mother. But what was she saying now?

Elida read the note several times and became more and more puzzled each time. The words were much too complex and the message, whatever it was, was much too profound for a child to have written. Elida then reminded herself of an important fact – this was not written by just any child.

Elida placed the envelope back in the drawer and walked to the office. She was relieved to find that the books on the shelf had not yet been packed. She reached up and pulled from the shelf the Bible, which she leafed through in search of the words that Paloma had written. After nearly a half an hour, she had found nothing that coincided to any significant degree.

She placed the Bible back on the shelf and pulled down *The Prophet*. By the evening, she had read the whole book but still had found nothing that could explain Paloma's note. In the library the next two days, she searched endlessly among the stacks of religious and psychological books and journals for some kind of explanation.

"Where did she get this wisdom?" Elida asked Orpet as they got into bed. "How could God have inspired her in such a way? She was just our little girl Orpet."

"It's beyond me Elida. Just the fact that she wrote these last notes with the obvious intention that you would find them after she died is miraculous. I wish I knew what to say honey."

"I don't think there's anything to say."

Orpet embraced his wife and they kissed, the first time they had really kissed in a long while. Their marriage and the love that they shared had been thrust into a cold and dark corner. As they kissed they realized that in each other they still had the bond that meant so much.

"God is testing us, Orpet. We have to continue to seek out the reasons."

Elida arrived at church early on Sunday and sat in the pew closest to the choir. As the choir began to sing, she remained quiet. Paloma did not want her to sing; she never did. It was the last thing she had said before she slipped away. It is the angels who sing and Elida was not an angel. She listened carefully to the sound of the choir. Perhaps she would hear Paloma's voice.

Her mind drifted throughout the chapel as the priest stood

and began reading from the Bible.

"We do not want you to be unaware, brothers, about those who have fallen asleep, so that you may not grieve like the rest, who have no hope. For if we believe that Jesus died and rose, so too will God, through Jesus, bring with him those who have fallen asleep..."

Elida's eyes perked up as she heard the words "hope" and "believe," then the priest began his sermon.

"It is here, in the first letter to the Thessalonians, that St. Paul reminds the Christians that in the face of death, they cannot behave like pagans who have no hope. But they need to believe that like Christ, those who die will also resurrect..."

Elida squirmed in her seat and looked directly into the eyes of the priest. She then unfolded the piece of paper that she clutched in her hands and read to herself the very words that the priest had just read:

"To believe is truth in a hope that we have the creation of life."
Signed: Paloma

Chapter 16

On a beautiful August morning in suburban São Paulo, on the patio of her brand new house, Elida sat alone in a comfortable lawn chair. As her daughter had done so many, many times in the past, Elida took out a clean white sheet of paper and began to write. She wrote to no one in particular or she wrote to everyone in general; she wasn't sure at the moment and it didn't really matter. For now, she just wrote.

> The sky is blue, the grass is green, the air is still and the day is warm. Everything seems to be in perfect order. And then I think of Paloma. Suddenly, everything seems to be in disorder. Or does it?
>
> I feel as if I've lived a century during these past three months. My head is like a labyrinth. But there is a way out and I will find it. If it takes until the very last minute of my life, I will find an understanding. I won't stop until I find the reason.
>
> Why did this happen to us? Why with me, who loved her so much? Our relationship was the most beautiful thing. We shared the same likes and tastes. We had the same way of thinking. Where I was, she was. The truth was that Paloma was still attached to me, as if the umbilical cord had never been severed. A short time ago I even told myself to keep some distance from her because she was growing up and she needed her own space. I thought to myself that if she stays too close to me, she'll suffer too much the day I die. How ironic this life is. Or is there such a thing as irony? Is

there such a thing as coincidences or luck or accidents? Or does everything happen for a reason, for a special purpose and as part of a special plan? I thank God I never moved away from her at that time. Those moments were precious and now they're all I've got to remember.

Paloma was not only my daughter, she was mine. All the love that I have for Orpet, Renata, and Tiago, and all the love they have for me cannot compare to what Paloma and I had. It was a total communion. We were one being. Our thoughts and our feelings were always in perfect harmony. Art united us and even today I feel proud of what her teacher had said of Paloma, that she was an artist. I felt proud when I realized that she had inherited something from me. But she had even more talent than I have because I never had all her capacity for sentiment and passion. Orpet and I had a great deal of pride in Paloma. Although many people never quite understood her, we always knew she was special and we always marveled in what she did. Orpet always said that Paloma would win big in life, and she did win. We are proud of that; a beautiful and sweet sense of pride.

Still, everyday when I wake up, I can't believe it. How can I exist without her? How can I continue living without her? How long do I have to live here and what do I have to do to be able to receive her again? I am living in two worlds, in two dimensions. I live here on Earth where my children need me and I live in a spiritual space in search of Paloma.

I suffer terribly and there is no money, no medicine, no science, nothing that will alleviate my pain. It is irreversible. Time cannot go back. All I can do is rely on my faith and pray that God will forgive me for my mistakes and terminate this pain in some way.

I do take comfort in knowing, and this I believe with absolute certainty, that Paloma's spirit is alive. I told Orpet that God put Paloma in our lives like a bait. He gave her to us and we loved her immensely and then he took her away in the moment that he wanted to. At the same time that I suffer, I begin to be happy for I know that she is living in a better world, a world that is so marvelous because one has God as a companion. That is extremely gratifying.

I gain a lot of strength by reading over again the letters and poems that Paloma wrote for me, although they increase the feelings of how much I miss her. They also help me understand that there is a special force behind everything that happened. The words she wrote to me were too deep and too profound for a normal 8-year-old girl. I had no way of believing them at the time, no way of interpreting them as a warning. I wish I had, but I was not privileged to the same special force that she was nor was I intended to interfere with it. Now, as I read them again and pay more attention to them, I sense that she wrote them as if she would be writing them now, after she's gone. That's quite amazing, if not miraculous. It's as if she left them for me to use as an aid to help me deal with my pain. This is something so powerful and so passionate and I will always treasure it.

These have been difficult moments for us. The children suffered so much and they still suffer. Time will be the best remedy for them. Renata surprised me with a maturity that I didn't expect. She gave me the most strength. I can never thank her enough for that. Tiago is getting stronger but he still cries a lot. It broke my heart to see him separated from a sister who he loved so much. I don't know any boy who was as close to a sister as he was to Paloma. He gave her attention and protection all the time. Now he has withdrawn. As I told Orpet, I believe that because of this, his childhood is over. Orpet has also suffered extremely although it has never been his nature to wear his feelings on his sleeve. But I sense his pain. He is very nervous and he needs a lot of rest. He needs more than me, for I have already found my pillow.

That is how things are. I am here, alone, trying now to carry on and seek the answers to the test that I've been given. It is so hard. My world is different...there are no more toys around the house...the ponies are quiet...there is no more pink...there are no more little braids for me to do and no more tiny laces to tie...there are no more unexpected kisses upon my cheek...My little doll is gone...My little pink doll is gone.

Chapter 17

Time heals all wounds.

Not so on the path to discovering the reasons to life's mysterious circumstances. Not so on the journey to spiritual consciousness and a higher self awareness. Not so along the road less traveled. And not so in the wake of Paloma's passing.

Through the grace of God, time will transpire on its own. Days will turn to nights and nights will turn to days without asking for our intervention. The passage of time is a passive act. It can heal nothing by itself. It can not empower or enlighten by itself. That requires self responsibility and self effort. That requires faith and hope and love.

And so it was in São Paulo, Brazil in May of 1996. As the days turned to nights, as Paloma's classmates moved through high school, as Renata and Tiago moved into adulthood and as Orpet and Elida moved on with their lives, time did not heal a thing. However faith and hope and love did.

But there were not wounds to heal. In a world that identifies the good with pleasure and the bad with pain, wounds can be inflicted. But in a world where it is understood that God's will involves tests, not accidents, and reasons, not coincidences, it's also understood that there is a spiritual solution to everything and that bliss can surface from turmoil and despair and even death.

J. Martin Kohe wrote in a series of lessons, when discussing the secret of dealing with trouble, "It is sometimes very hard to understand the death of a loved one but with confident and sound reasoning, before long, the lesson which is to be taught becomes visible and apparent so that we are able to go about our business with a faith that is unwavering."

The late Joseph, Cardinal Bernardin found his spiritual solution while he lived with the despair of terminal cancer. Said he, "Some see death as an enemy. Others see it as a friend. As a person of faith who views death as simply the transition from the physical life to eternal life, I see death as a friend."

Another spiritual solution comes from M. Scott Peck in *The Road Less Traveled*. Peck refers in part to Carlos Casteneda's The Teachings of Don Juan, when he describes "death as our 'ally,' still fearsome but continually a source of wise counsel. With death's counsel, the constant awareness of the limit of our time to live and love, we can always be guided to make the best use of our time and live life to the fullest. But if we are unwilling to fully face the fearsome presence of death on our left shoulder, we deprive ourselves of its counsel and cannot possibly live or love with clarity. When we shy away from death, the ever-changing nature of things, we inevitably shy away from life."

Elida pursued her spiritual solution with a daily passion. Why did this happen? What is the meaning of it? What is the meaning of Paloma's life and death? The answers and reasons for her would come in their proper time and in their proper way. Through the process and through the years, Elida felt stronger inside. She grew and she changed. Life was no longer a day to day routine towards a comfortable existence filled with superficial pursuits. There was much more. There was meaning and there was purpose.

For her, religion was a major part of that. To understand God's will Elida put God in the place where he should have always been – first. The Cross filled her heart in the way that Paloma taught. She filled her heart with love and faith and hope. The Bible says that "faith can move mountains." Saint John said that "the truth shall make you free." Saint Paul spoke of "belief and hope" in the first letter to the Thessalonians. Paloma, an 8-year-old philosopher with no formal religious training, said the same things to her mother in her own mixture of words and ideas: "To believe is truth in a hope that we have the creation of life."

The power and mysticism of Paloma's words and thoughts enlightened Elida in the same way that the words and thoughts of the greatest scholars, educators and religious leaders have done for many, throughout the years.

Napoleon Hill, in his timeless work *Think and Grow Rich*, mirrored Paloma's thoughts about belief, faith, hope and creation by saying, "Faith is the 'eternal elixir' which gives life, power, and action to the impulse of thought!"

And there is this beautiful passage by Sogyal Rinpoche from *The Tibetan Book of Living and Dying*, which could very well be applied to a description of Paloma:

"In the modern world, there are few examples of human beings who embody the qualities that come from realizing the nature of the mind. So it is hard for us to even imagine enlightenment or the perception of an enlightened being, and even harder to begin to think that we ourselves could be enlightened...Even if we were to think of the possibility of enlightenment, one look at what composes our ordinary mind–anger, greed, jealousy, spite, cruelty, lust, fear, anxiety, and turmoil–would undermine forever any hope of achieving it...Enlightenment...is real; and each of us, whoever we are, can in the right circumstances and with the right training realize the nature of mind and so know in us what is deathless and eternally pure. This is the promise of all the mystical traditions of the world, and it has been fulfilled and is being fulfilled in countless thousands of human lives."

Without question, it was fulfilled in Elida's life and in the life of her "deathless and eternally pure" angel, Paloma.

"We are so fortunate that life offers us a new start with every new day," Elida said. "Make the most of that. Go forward in your life with a renewed spirit, free from fear, and you will find light at the end of each tunnel, sunshine with each new dawn. I can tell you that as you go forward, you will not be alone. There is a force in you and with you that will guide you, provided, that you believe it. Trust me when I tell you that there is no punishment; only blessing. In my journey, whenever pain tries to overshadow joy, I reach for the truth that's been revealed to me and I find happiness.

"When I was a young girl I tried to put a bouquet of pink roses onto the altar in my church. It wasn't a big deal at the time, but I always remember it. Paloma loved pink and she made me remember those pink flowers. I couldn't reach the altar back then and I had to place the flowers on the floor. Today, my flowers are no longer on the floor. They are on the altar to the glory of God.

"God looks for vases to put his flowers in. Think about that. What does that mean? For me, God's flowers are all the many blessings that he can give to us. We are the vases. God tries to deliver his flowers but sometimes we are not the vases that we need to be. Other times, God gives us the flowers but then takes them away. I know. Paloma was my pink flower.

"What is it to lose a flower? It is to gain the knowledge of the vase you need to be.

"What is it to lose a daughter? It is to gain the heavens."

About The Author

Rich Winograd lives in Thousand Oaks, California and is a sales executive for a major U.S. corporation. He is a graduate of the University of Southern California, where he met his wife, Regina. They have two daughters, Deborah and Tatiana. Rich became Paloma's uncle through marriage (Regina and Paloma's father, Orpet, are sister and brother) and was inspired to write this book after learning of Paloma's story. *Paloma* is his only book.

Rich has studied and followed the teachings of Napoleon Hill for most of his adult life. He read *Think and Grow Rich* and Napoleon Hill's other great book, *The Master Key to Riches,* for the first time over 20 years ago and has re-read each of these books, which he keeps in his office, many times over the past 20 years. "They have been extremely important to my personal development and without question, instrumental in writing *Paloma.*"

As the Napoleon Hill World Learning Center at Purdue University Calumet, our goal is to disseminate Napoleon Hill's works to all audiences that are open and interested. Currently, our focus is on the general student and correctional populations nationwide. Youth and adult programs are available as specially arranged seminars as well. Instructors in your area are available to work within your budget and program requirements. For special requests, please contact us at nhf@calumet.purdue.edu.

Also Available From the Napoleon Hill World Learning Center

BOOKS

Think and Grow Rich
Yearly Inspirational Calendar
You Can
Your Greatest Power
How to Become a Mental Millionaire
Timeless Thoughts for Today
Wake Up! You're Alive
Beyond Positive Thinking
Making Miracles
52 Lessons for Life
Paloma

COURSES

PMA – Science of Success Course – Home Study Kit
PMA – Distance Learning Course – (Keys to Success)
Leader Certification Seminar
Beginner, Intermediate, and Advanced Programs
For the 17 Success Principles – Instructor Led

PRISON POPULATION COURSES

Correctional Courses and Materials Nationwide
For incarcerated youth and adults
Domestic Violence Center Programs

MEMBERSHIP

Mastermind Online at www.naphill.org

For additional information about Napoleon Hill products please contact the following locations:

Napoleon Hill World Learning Center
Purdue University Calumet
2300 173rd Street
Hammond, IN 46323-2094

Judith Williamson, Director
Uriel "Chino" Martinez, Assistant/Graphic Designer

Telephone: 219-989-3173 or 219-989-3166
email: nhf@calumet.purdue.edu

Napoleon Hill Foundation
University of Virginia-Wise
College Relations Apt. C
1 College Avenue
Wise, VA 24293

Don Green, Executive Director
Annedia Sturgill, Executive Assistant

Telephone: 276-328-6700
email: napoleonhill@uvawise.edu

Website: www.naphill.org